They lied to you about high fidelity!

It's true. The world's largest and richest corporations (how do you suppose they *got* rich?) have lied to you about what high fidelity is, what it can do for you and how you can get it. They've told you it was buttons, lights, meters, digital readouts, and loud, loud sounds. They *didn't* tell you it was *music:* melody, harmony and rhythm. They've cheated you...and maybe they've gotten away with it.

Until now.

The UHF Guide to Ultra High Fidelity is from the people who have made *Ultra High Fidelity Magazine* a huge success. This guide will tell you:

—How to set up a system that can make a forty year old analog disc sound *better* than today's Compact Discs.

—Why the people who invented CD don't know how to play them right...and how it *can* be done.

—How most amplifiers are built by people who flunked physics...and how to find an amp that wasn't.

—How to tell a good loudspeaker from a disco boom box (*Hint:* don't bother reading the specifications).

—How to literally change your life by bringing *live music* into your home.

But that's only the beginning!

To my parents, who bemusedly allowed me to dismantle our first "hi-fi" system, to the countless people who knew more than I did and who taught me all I know about hi-fi, and to Dr. Pat Shaw, without whose fabulous record collection I would never have discovered high fidelity in the first place.

G.R.

Broadcast Canada
Box 316, Station A
Longueuil, Québec, Canada J4H 3Z2

ISBN: 0–9694792–0–4

Cartoons: Khurram Z. Syed
Cover design: Jacques Millette, *Covigraff*
Printed and bound in Canada by *L'éclaireur*

Table of contents

The
UHF Guide
to
Ultra High Fidelity

edited by
Gerard Rejskind

BROADCAST CANADA

Foreword

Do you loathe hi-fi? Do you consider hi-fi gear to be an expensive, bulky, ugly, loud, raucous intrusion on your personal space? Would you rather enjoy music than listen to equipment?

Do you go to live concerts and get caught up in the excitement of the music? Do you ever wish the records you play at home could catch you up in the same sort of excitement?

Good!

We wrote this guide for you.

Why are we offering a guide to high fidelity when we already publish an entire magazine about hi-fi every two months? It's because we realize that no magazine can do the job by itself. The task we've embarked on is an ambitious one: not simply to cater to a community, but to create one and define it.

why we're doing
this

Very simply, *Ultra High Fidelity Magazine* is intended to recruit people to the cause of genuine high fidelity. Not that hi-fi will ever be a mainstream activity. Frankly, if you use music as a cheerful background noise, you might as well put this volume back on the shelf and move on to the Garfield books. But then again, maybe you use music as a background because the music you hear at home isn't worth your full attention. In which case step right up to the bookstore checkout. I think I can promise this guide will be money well spent.

What I, my colleagues and most of our readers have learned about hi-fi is so little-known that you could almost call it a closely-guarded secret. It is this. You can make music in your home sound live. You can forget about the buttons and the decibels and the specifications, and get caught up in the same sort of excitement you've felt in the presence of live musicians. Doing this does *not* require filling your

4

home with ugly boxes that radiate red points of light, it need *not* get you into irrevocable trouble with your neighbors and landlord, and it does *not* require you to deal with fast-talking salesmen in loud checked jackets. And although it will certainly cost you some money, it does *not* demand that you become a millionaire first.

How is it done? That's what this book is about. We will tell you how the stuff they're trying to sell you really works, and let you know what we've discovered. You won't need an engineering degree to understand it, but all the technical details are here if you want them.

how can you be sure we're right?

Everything we will tell you, you can check out for yourself. But be aware of one thing: most of it will be at odds with what you've read and heard elsewhere. We will tell you that you have been lied to about high fidelity — by manufacturers, by distributors, by salesmen, by magazines, by the richest people in the electronics industry. Which is, incidentally, how they got rich. You may not believe everything we tell you — not at first. But we encourage you to read, and to verify everything you read.

If you love music you won't be sorry.

Gerard Rejskind
Editor in chief
ULTRA HIGH FIDELITY MAGAZINE

Foreword

What is hi-fi?

What *is* high fidelity?

Can we begin a book on this subject without de-fining high fidelity itself? We do intend to innovate, but we don't want to scare you off in the very first paragraph of chapter one, so here goes the usual. *High fidelity is the closest possible approach to the original sound.*

You say you're not satisfied with that definition? Neither are we. Most record producers are not *trying* to capture a close approximation of the original sound, because there may not be an original sound to approximate. With so much rock music "composed" on a 32-track recorder as much as on a musical instrument, what does "fidelity" mean? When the software has everything but monosodium glutamate added, why should the equipment that plays it back be natural?

But it *should* be, for a good reason which has everything to do with our own definition of hi-fi. Music played back on a high fidelity system will be more enjoyable than it will be on any other system, *no matter how expensive.* It will touch your emotions more. You will hear more of its melody, its harmony, even its rhythm. A high fidelity system is a *musical* system.

musicality

What makes equipment "musical?" There are nu-merous theories, but so far they have all proven incomplete, if not utterly wrong, which is why we have struck out on our own, first with a magazine, and now with this book. We want to tell you what hi-fi is, how to spot it when you hear it, how to get it for yourself. We will be giving you lots of technical information, though, because a lot of people use en-gineering jargon to lie to you; we want you to be ready for them.

Let's begin by looking closely at the job a music system must do.

defining music

Music can be defined by just two variables: frequency, and amplitude. Frequency is the same thing as musical pitch, of course, and it's a familiar word. Amplitude is less familiar in popular language. It will probably be called "volume" or "loudness" when it refers to sound. It will more likely be called "level" when it refers to a stream of electrons running about the equipment.

frequency

Music varies tremendously in frequency. Middle C has a frequency of 256 Hz. You'll hear a 1000 Hz tone when a TV station is transmitting color bars before the broadcast day starts. And the highest sound you can hear is around 15 kHz...perhaps a little more if you're under 30 years of age and don't operate a pneumatic drill for a living. Few musical instruments go below 100 Hz. A piano can but seldom does — ever notice how the keys on the extreme left are usually cleaner than the rest? However a kick drum or a string bass may drop as low as 35 Hz, and a 32-foot organ pipe (found only in the largest churches) can produce sound of 16 Hz. At that frequency it is hard to say if we are still "hearing," since the whole body reacts to such vibrations.

amplitude

Amplitude is a little more difficult to explain. Electronic signals are measured in absolute units such as volts or watts...and relations between two levels are stated in decibels. However when we are talking about actual sounds rather than electrical signals, we use a unit called the dBa (often mistakenly written as simply dB). A dBa resembles the dB (80 dBa is ten times as loud as 70 dBa) but it is an absolute unit like volts and watts, not a *relative* unit. The dBa is arranged so that 0 dBa is the threshold of human hearing. Note that this is rock bottom *only* for humans; a level one tenth as loud as 0 dBa would be -10 dBa. From the threshold of hearing to the threshold of pain, there is a loudness difference of nearly 4,000,000,000,000 times! See the reason for the invention of the dBa? Isn't it easier to say 115 dB?

Fortunately hi-fi equipment won't be called upon to reproduce such an awesome ratio of signal levels. Musical information typically varies from 25 dBa (the ambient noise of a good recording studio) to the 105 dBa of a large orchestra heard from a good seat. This is still a difference of 80 dB, however, or 100,000,000 times. You can see what audio designers are up against.

Is that really all a hi-fi system has to do — reproduce the frequencies and the loudness correctly? Yes that's all. And providing it doesn't also add other stuff that's not in the program, it will sound perfect. But since that isn't possible — and never will be possible — it doesn't help us much with our real-life definition of high fidelity.

All right, then, hi-fi equipment isn't perfect, but don't the magazines define hi-fi as the closest possible approach to perfection? And can't that be measured by technical instruments?

No it can't.

the limits of
instruments

Yes, we know magazines are trying to do it, and indeed are claiming to succeed. They measure everything there is about an audio component, and they base their conclusions on that, sometimes not even bothering to listen to music through it. This leads them to strange conclusions. Because they believe what the instruments tell them, they conclude that modern amplifiers are within an insignificant hair of perfection, and that Compact Disc players are so perfect that — inevitably — they all sound virtually alike. In reaching these conclusions they frequently ignore the evidence of their own ears.

It is also part of their credo that the ear is a lousy diagnostic instrument, insensitive to most forms of distortion, with a poor capacity for comparison, easily influenced by mood and visual cues, as well as by social and psychological factors.

the right way to
evaluate

These things are not true either, and that is why some years ago we launched our own magazine. We know how to read instruments, and of course we own a number of them, but we don't let them write the articles. We propose a different test, one that you can use yourself: *actually listening to music.*

Is listening an unreliable method? Not in our experience. We use a panel of listeners in our tests, and with few exceptions we have been able to get broad agreement. Indeed, we have performed blind tests using both experts and neophytes, and neither group had much difficulty hearing differences among components.

Yes...but why *doesn't* measurement work? Well it does, of course, providing you're measuring the right thing, but what *is* the right thing? There are hundreds of potential tests you could do, most of them with instruments that you don't have or that don't exist. Naturally people tend to test with what they actually have or can buy, but the result won't help predict how much fun you'll have when you actually listen to music.

where to go

Be prepared to use your ears, then. But where? How? If you do some listening at most stores, you'll be in for a disappointment. You won't be able to decide what's better. Therein lies the greatest barrier between you and high fidelity.

Where to hear hi-fi

If you are new to the restrained circle of genuine high fidelity, then you probably know "hi-fi" from those technoid stores with glitzy components in the window, overhung with large backlit signs bearing the names of large international corporations, whose rooms are full of receivers and loudspeakers.

Perhaps you've wandered in and had a listen. You may have been vaguely aware that what you heard was somewhat "better" (that is, louder, bassier and brighter) than the sounds coming from your own record player or radio. But after a quick demonstration via the store's "comparator" box, you may have been at a loss to tell what was better. You may therefore have concluded that you don't have the "trained ear" needed to tell the difference between mediocrity and true high fidelity.

Actually you do.

The reason you couldn't hear any appreciable difference among those different combinations is that there wasn't any. *None* of them sounded like music. *All* of them were collections of distortions and noise. When your ear told you there was no difference, it was telling you the truth.

Why are those systems so bad? Why aren't most stores able to demonstrate hi-fi?

There's worse. Most large international corporations do not build high fidelity equipment. They could, of course, because they have the necessary resources, but they don't think there's much money in it. They get much richer by building products intended for the eye rather than the ear, products that test perfectly but sound terrible.

Sound terrible? Are we saying that the majority of famous-name stereo receivers sound poor, that most of those glistening Japanese speakers are awful, and that manufacturers *deliberately* make them sound horrible?

Yes. We are, and they do.

It's not hard to see why. The way to move a large volume of merchandise is to sell through chains of high-volume dealers who take low markups. In order to survive on those low markups, of course, they can't spend precious space on good listening rooms, or much time serving customers. The buyer must be seduced fast, and the fastest way is through the eyes. Hence the complex control panels of many amplifiers and receivers, which are ergonomic horrors even their designers couldn't operate without the instruction manual. Naturally these units cannot be optimized for sound quality. The profit margins on mass-market gear are low, all the available money has been spent on the looks, and anyway the salesmen will have neither time nor space to demonstrate it adequately. How to convince the buyer of the superior quality of the unit, then? Simple — *tell* him it's good. Design it so that it will measure extremely well on certain tests. Print those amazing specifications in your advertising, and get audio magazines financed with that same advertising to run "test reports" confirming that your unit performs as advertised.

irrelevant tests

As we shall see, measuring beautifully on certain selected tests has little to do with audible performance. Indeed, excellent specs are often gained at the expense of the sound. That's why we say that most equipment is deliberately designed to sound poor.

discovering hi-fi

Fortunately there are stores which don't operate this way, stores that stock genuine hi-fi components, which are capable of playing for you what you will easily recognize as lifelike music. In the pages of this book we will introduce you to this equipment and to the people who sell it. We will explain how it works, why it sounds the way it does, and how it should be listened to. We will put you on the trail of discovery. Best of all, we will tell you how you can set up in your own home an audio system that will play real music.

It is not an exaggeration to say that it can enrich your life. It has enriched ours.

Turntables

You might wonder why, in the age of digital media, we are including a chapter on turntables so early in the book. Isn't the vinyl disc passé?

Not exactly.

is analog dead?

Regular readers of our magazine will know that for years we have been fighting the notion that digital sound is inherently superior to the older "analog" recording systems. Since this book includes an entire section on digital sound we won't belabor the point just now, but we can sum it up this way. The vinyl disc is inferior to the Compact Disc in only one important way: its vulnerability to surface blemishes. In every other way which has to do with music, it is demonstrably superior. If you're not aware of this, it is because you have not heard a turntable that can play back a record properly. The vast majority of turntables, like so many other components, are deliberately made to sound bad. This may sound incredible, but we will invite you to prove it for yourself.

the importance of the source

The other reason for the high profile given the turntable chapter is this: it is one of our tenets that the music source is the most important part of a music system. This runs directly counter to the claim by mainstream salesmen and magazines that the loudspeaker is the most important part. but there is no way a loudspeaker can possibly correct something that has gone wrong at the source. The loudspeaker *cannot* restore information that the source has failed to extract. If you have a poor source and a good speaker, you will merely hear with devastating clarity and fidelity just how bad your source is. In fact this is exactly what happens in mediocre systems. You *must* improve a system starting by its source, for the same reason that you begin purifying a river by its source, and not by its mouth.

12

The turntable

Let's take a turntable apart, so that we are clear on the names of the different parts, and on the role each one plays.

less simple than it looks

The role of the turntable *looks* simple enough, and in fact most magazines grossly oversimplify it. In their view it suffices that the turntable should spin the disc at a perfectly even speed, and avoid adding audible motor noise to the sound. That is all. And since instruments exist for measuring those aspects of its performance, it hardly seems necessary to listen to the turntable at all.

Here's what these magazines (and the manufacturers themselves) will measure.

turntable speed

Speed accuracy. If there isn't a variable speed control, is the speed accurate? Any error will be expressed as a percentage.

Does it *remain* accurate? The speed drift over time will also be expressed as a percentage.

wow and flutter

Does the speed oscillate back and forth? Inevitably it will. If the variation is a slow one, caused perhaps by a slight eccentricity in the platter, it will be called *wow,* which is onomatopoeia for the effect it produces. A rapid variation will be called *flutter.* Both wow and flutter will also be expressed as a percentage of the nominal speed. Instruments exist to measure all of these flaws.

rumble

The other measure you'll see is rumble. This is usually caused by motor vibration getting into the platter, and hence into the music. Rumble will be expressed as a noise figure (in decibels) with a minus sign in front of it. For instance, if the rumble figure is -55 dB, this means that the measured motor vibration is 55 decibels lower than the test tone on a standard record. This is quite easy to measure, (and naturally all turntables are designed to shine on such measurements) but the very existence of this test has made turntables sound far worse than they once did.

Remember that most consumers buy with their eyes rather than their ears. They don't have to be technicians to be impressed with published performance figures...which are designed to fool them. So let us explain *how* they're trying to fool you, and *why*.

driving the platter

Each turntable has a motor and a platter, and somehow the motor must be made to turn the platter at the correct speed. There are three ways of doing this. You can use an *idler* (a rubber tire) to transfer the power from the motor shaft to the rim of the platter. This yields high torque and quick acceleration, but it doesn't isolate the platter much, and so it is used only on a few (very poor) broadcast turntables. A *drive belt* can be used to couple a pulley on the motor shaft to the larger platter. Finally, there is the very popular *direct drive,* in which the platter itself is the rotor of the motor. The reason for the popularity of direct drive is that it yields the very best rumble figures.

But *why should it?* When the disc is resting on the motor itself, why doesn't direct drive yield the poorest performance of all? It does, in fact, but it yields Good Numbers. This paradox explains why consumers are being fooled into accepting increasingly poor sound.

measuring rumble

The straightforward way to measure turntable rumble is this. You play a tone from a test recording, and set your decibel meter to 0 dB. You then play a silent band on the same record (at which time you are presumably reading only motor noise), and you note the new reading. The difference is the rumble figure.

lying with figures

But that figure doesn't look very good. On most turntables it will be in the order of −35 dB or even −30 dB. Consumers who are used to seeing noise figures of −80 dB on amplifiers, and −65 dB even on cassette decks, might wonder why turntables are so noisy. So a bit of diddling is done before the figure finds its way into print. The diddling goes by the name of *weighting*.

The rationale is this. Most rumble is made up of low frequency sounds. But the ear is not especially sensitive to low frequencies, and anyway most loudspeakers won't reproduce extreme lows, so why should all frequencies carry the same weight? To compensate for the ear's dropping sensitivity at low frequencies, manufacturers mark "on the curve," just as teachers do. A filter is placed in the meter circuit so that it will de-emphasize the low frequencies, and thereby some of the rumble. There is a standard curve for doing this: the "A" curve established by the German industrial standards agency, *DIN*. Which is why you may see a rumble figure shown as –55 dB, (DIN A). That is, of course, the same –35 dB figure, "improved" by one hundred times.

bigger lies

But that "improvement" is not good enough for most manufacturers. There also exists a DIN B curve, which is so attractive it is downright seductive. Measuring on the DIN B curve, you virtually filter out the bottom end of the audible spectrum entirely. The figure will now be, perhaps, –75 dB (DIN B).

And this is where direct drive comes in.

It's obvious that a direct-drive turntable will feed *tremendous* amounts of vibration into the platter. However that vibration will be very low in pitch, because the motor is turning at 33 1/3 rpm instead of (typically) 1600 rpm. The lower the pitch, the more it is disregarded by an instrument measuring on the curve. So direct drive is widely used because it yields terrific numbers, even though in fact it is as much as *ten times worse* than a belt-driven turntable.

But is that so bad? If there is no one to hear a tree falling in the forest, does it make a sound? Who cares about vibration if it's not audible?

Well, look at it this way. The music is represented on a vinyl disc by a little squiggle in a groove. The subtle nuances are even smaller squiggles, so tiny they won't be noticed under a microscope. It takes an extraordinarily sensitive vibration pickup system to detect and reproduce these tiny vibrations. What happens to them if they are swamped by much larger outside vibrations from the drive motor?

They are lost. You may not hear the motor noise, but nor will you hear the musical detail. This will cost you in every single respect. You will not hear the harmony, you will have more trouble following the melody, and you may even have trouble making out the rhythm of the music. You won't hear anything that is much softer than the maximum level of the music. Many of the overtones will vanish, as will depth cues, stereo (three-dimensional) information — in short much of what's been recorded.

It is possible to use direct drive in a high-quality turntable, but it is an engineering challenge of awesome proportions, with a suitably awesome price tag. At more reasonable prices, a musical turntable can be driven only by a belt.

Unfortunately the motor is not the only source of unwanted vibration. It may not even be the principal one. "Bad vibes" also come from the bearing, from the loudspeakers, and from the record itself.

In a properly-designed belt-driven turntable, the motor is so decoupled from the platter that it might as well not exist...but the record is riding right on the bearing. No decoupling is possible. Somehow that bearing has to be kept quiet, and unfortunately there is no cheap way to do this.

The first of the modern high-quality turntables to be made, nearly two decades ago, was the *Linn* Sondek, whose success was partly based on its bearing design. The shaft of the pivot was tapered, so that a small tip turned on the bearing at the bottom of the bearing well. Because the circumference of the pivot bottom was so small, its angular (rotary) speed was also small, and vibration was reduced.

making a quiet bearing

There are other ways to accomplish the same thing. For instance, one excellent turntable has a ball bearing permanently fasted to the pivot's bottom. It rotates against another ball bearing. Of course, because the contact area is so small, there is a good deal of pressure on that poor little bearing. The materials used must be exceptionally hard and durable, or else they won't last.

still more vibrations

There is another important source of vibration: the loudspeakers, and the rest of the planet. These vibrations can be so violent that under some circumstances they will be only a little lower in level than the music itself.

dealing with vibration

One way to keep them out of the record-playing system is with some sort of energy-absorbing suspension. The drawing on this page indicates one common method of doing this. The turntable bearing, platter and tone arm are mounted on a subchassis, made of something exceptionally rigid so it won't twist. The subchassis is suspended from the plinth by springs, which act as mechanical filters

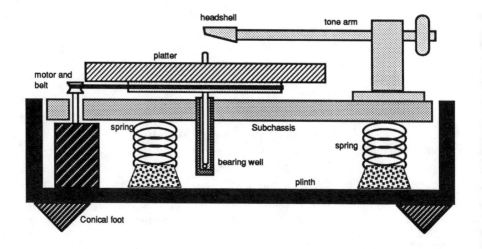

against the world. Unfortunately a well-designed spring suspension is expensive, and it is difficult to adjust properly. Each of the three (sometimes four) springs must be "tuned" for proper performance. That should generally be left to a competent dealer.

There are alternatives to a spring suspension. One very good moderately-priced turntable has its components mounted on a wood slab that is fastened to a lower wood slab through resilient bushings. Large rubber-like feet also help filter out vibration. Finally, one turntable is simply built into what looks like a giant block of solid marble. That's heavy but seems effective.

a new test

In our magazine testing program, we designed an innovative test for turntable suspensions. We placed the turntable on a loudspeaker, and put the arm in the groove of an immobilized record. We then played tones of different frequencies through the speaker to see how much got through the turntable suspension to the arm. One of the best turntables we've tested gave us this result.

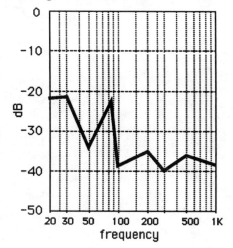

As you can see, frequencies ranging from 30 Hz to 1 kHz are nicely filtered out. We were a little less thrilled with the results of a second turntable, whose suspension ceases to operate at certain frequencies.

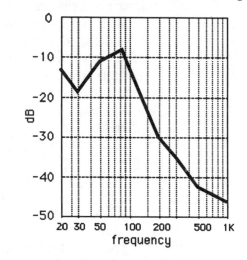

how bad can it get?

But even that is quite wonderful compared to the result we got with one expensive Japanese-built direct-drive turntable.

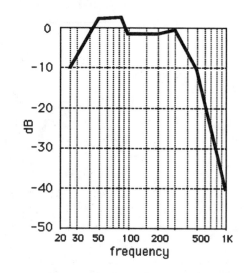

As you can see, at low frequencies the vibrations coming up through the ineffective spring suspension were actually louder than the music! To put it another way, that turntable's vulnerability to low-pitched vibration was *over a million times greater* than that of the turntable in the first diagram. You can well expect that the first turntable would deliver quite a bit more in the way of musical detail.

one last source of
vibrations

There's also a final source of vibration: the stylus in the groove itself. The stylus is riding along in a miniature canyon whose sides are pressing the stylus to move up and down and from side to side. The stylus pushes back, as Newton's First Law says it must. There's a tiny shock wave that goes out from the contact point. But of course it comes back.

What happens when it comes back? It is a little echo of the original...or it *would* be if there were only one wave coming back. In fact there will be many, whose times of arrival will depend on where they've been in the meantime. They may also bring with them other sounds. For instance, if the platter rings like a dinner gong, some of its metallic ringing will accompany the returning wave. All of this will be quite a bit softer than the main music signal itself, but it may be louder than the tiny nuances that give the music its distinctiveness. And if so it will wipe them out.

damping the
record

There are different solutions to this problem, and turntable designers get into arguments as to which is best. You can place the disc against a very heavy non-resonant platter. The radical change of mass where the light record meets the platter will act as a reflective barrier. The vibrations will of course be reflected back into the record, but at least they'll get back *quickly* and won't smear the sound quite as much. You can also press the record tightly against a soft, rubbery record mat, which will absorb the energy from the vibration so that it won't be echoed back at all. Note that such a mat must not have ridges or ribs (as most turntable mats in fact do) but must on

20

the contrary be perfectly smooth. The record will have to adhere very tightly to the mat. For that reason some turntables include either a weight or a clamp to press the two together. At least two turntables actually have tiny (inaudible?) vacuum pumps to suck the disc down!

Finally, one turntable maker argues that air is the best damping material of all, and has no platter at all. The record is supported only by the centre.

record mats

A word on record mats. As you may have gathered, different mats are designed to do quite different things. Soft rubbery mats are meant to damp out the vibrations travelling through the disc. A simple felt mat may be used to keep a metal platter from ringing. High-mass platters, on the other hand, may work best with no mat at all. A mat meant for some other kind of turntable may make your own turntable sound worse.

We've heard too many turntables, good and bad, to pontificate dogmatically about which method is *The Right Way* to play a record. But we *do* know that the turntable is the most important component in any audio system that uses vinyl discs as a source, and we know how to recognize a good one. The highs will be clear and precise, without exaggeration. The midrange will be smooth and clean. The bottom end will be rich and detailed but not boomy. Melodies will be easy to hum along with, the most complex rhythms will be easy to follow, and — with a good recording — it will be easy to tell where each instrument was located.

how important is the turntable?

But how much of this is due to the turntable?

Some years ago we tested a number of turntables by our usual panel method. To make things easy for ourselves we recorded the same music from each turntable on high-speed high-quality open-reel tape, which could be played for all the panelists. At the end of the the tests, we played the tape through a

Chapter 2: Turntables

tiny system, consisting of a cheap amp and small *Radio Shack* speakers. No one had any trouble telling the (unidentified) turntables apart. The winner of the main test was readily spotted as the best turntable in this demonstration too.

The lesson? Get the best turntable you can possibly work into your budget. Even if you have to play it through a ghetto blaster for the first two years, its quality won't be wasted.

The tone arm
by Robert Franner

On the surface designing a tone arm looks easy. Unfortunately a lot of companies think it *is* easy. And they don't put all of the designing firepower that this high-technology product deserves and requires. The result is…well…

no perfect arms

The requirements of tone arm design are so stringent that there is no such thing as the perfect tone arm. Indeed, as we shall see, the requirements of tone arm design are essentially conflicting. That established, let's look at the attributes a "perfect" tone arm would have.

Rigidity. The tone arm must be inherently rigid, from the tip of the headshell through the bearings, all the way to the base. There must be no "play" in the bearings. If the arm moves even infinitesimally while absorbing the energy of the stylus, it will cancel out some stylus motion and effectively erase some of the information on your disc.

Infinite mass. In order to provide a maximum amount of information retrieval, the cartridge must remain absolutely stationary while the stylus kicks about in its groove. As we add mass to the cartridge body (by coupling it to the tone arm), we increase the mechanical impedance to such unwanted motion (or simply to resonances). The greater the mass, the better the tone arm can absorb and dissipate the energy fed into it by the cartridge.

Zero mass. When encountering record warps, the stylus will be driven into the cartridge body while moving uphill, thus causing the production of unwanted subsonic signals, and increasing stylus and record wear, due to the momentary increase in tracking force. After the hump, the reverse happens. A massive arm with a high moment of inertia will cause the downforce to be drastically reduced (in some cases it may be negative) during descent, resulting in a corresponding increase in stylus and groove wear. The smaller the combined arm/ cartridge mass, the less force there will be driving the stylus into the cartridge body on warp ascent. The same holds true for warp descent. Once the stylus has cleared the hump and is left standing in mid-air, the only force that acts upon it to bring it down again is the tracking downforce. This is usually 15 to 20 milliNewtons (often and incorrectly referred to as 1.5 or 2 grams — the gram is a unit of *mass,* not force). I harp on this point because many audiophiles believe that it is the force of gravity that brings the arm down to earth, in which case a heavier (more massive) arm/cartridge would fall at the same rate as a lighter combination (because the force of gravity is proportional to mass). But this is not the case, so only an arm/cartridge with *no mass at all* would be unaffected by warps.

Non-resonant construction. Once the energy from the cartridge has been transmitted to the arm, it may reflect back if it causes the arm itself to resonate. Rigid materials are inherently more resonant than softer substances...as you'll discover if you tap a crystal goblet and you tap a ball of Plasticine. An arm of a Plasticine-like material would be less prone to resonances than one of metal.

Zero friction. Friction in the vertical plane would defeat all of the advantages of our zero-mass tone arm, because the stylus would be driven into the cartridge body in fighting the drag of the bearing on warp ascent, and the 15 mN downforce would be diverted from its job of forcing the stylus to the groove during descent. Therefore, only with zero friction *and* zero mass would we experience no problems with warps.

Of course most of these parameters are mutually exclusive, and hence no such thing as a perfect tone arm could exist. As an interesting aside, what would be the sound produced by a zero friction/zero mass tone arm? No sound at all — and not only because such a design could exist only in theory. A zero mass/friction arm would move in unison with the cantilever as it traced the groove. Hence there would be no cantilever motion with respect to its generating system, and hence no output. Similarly, rigidity works against low-resonance; bearing friction goes up as play is reduced (hence there is tradeoff between rigidity and friction), and so on.

no "best" arm

To make matters more complicated, there is no set of tradeoffs that will make an arm the best compromise for all cartridges or turntables.

The audiophile or retailer who touts rigidity as the single most important virtue in a tone arm forgets that, as with chains, rigidity is lost if there is a weak link. That weak link could exist in many places outside of the tone arm, including the turntable subchassis, the platter, the mat, the vinyl record, and even the first line of defense: the cartridge body itself. What's the point of insisting on an ultra-rigid arm (which will necessarily have sacrificed some other important parameters in order to get that rigidity) if the cartridge body itself is of flimsy construction? The flimsiness of many a cartridge can be easily determined by twisting it in the headshell: if you can feel it move at all after you tighten the screws, a high-rigidity arm may not effect an intelligent compromise in the context of your system. Even if the cartridge body seems secure, there may lie weaknesses within the body. Most removable-stylus cartridges are inherently un-rigid where the stylus slides into the body. Some fixed-stylus moving-coil designs fare little better. A few years ago I cracked open an MC cartridge to find that its generating system (magnets, pole pieces and the entire stylus/cantilever assembly) had been tacked onto a little plastic tab that hung down from the plastic top. No wonder tightening the body into the headshell didn't make any difference!

do-it-yourself fixes

Applying a mastic substance such as Plasticine in the area of the headshell as a cure-all for resonances can lead to a decrease in performance as easily as not. Damping materials are only minimally effective when they are not in the direct path of energy transmission. Sticking Plasticine all over a headshell will do little to subdue resonances (although it will do a lot to increase effective mass), but sticking it between a cartridge and headshell will. Not that, in such a case, you will have introduced a direct tradeoff between information retrieval (because the cartridge/headshell connection will now be less rigid) and coloration. The same tradeoff will exist in designs that have a rubber grommet separating the headshell and arm tube, and/or between the arm base and the turntable.

matching the arm to the turntable

Some tone arms work better on some turntables than others. This is particularly true today, now that sprung-subchassis belt-driven turntables hold a virtual monopoly in audiophile systems. Many sprung-subchassis turntables (without arms) employ fixed springs that have been selected to support the entire mass of a particular (or average) tone arm assembly. If a competing model that is appreciably lighter or heavier is substituted, it can throw the subchassis equilibrium out of whack, compromising the feedback-filtering capability of the turntable.

Sometimes the perceived audible advantages arising from different tone arm compromises can vary because of interactions with other system components that lie totally outside the disc-playing system itself. Let's look at a hypothetical example. Two audiophiles, whom we'll call John and Bill, have identical turntables and electronics. Both employ the same two-way speakers, but Bill additionally has a subwoofer crossed over at around 125 Hz. Each is given two arms — one a high-mass, rigid design, the other of much lower mass — to try out with their moving-coil cartridges, and they compare notes. John reports that he prefers the low-mass design, claiming that, although it sounds more "frazzled," this is by far preferable to the "muffled" sound exhibited by the higher-mass design. He claims that the low-mass arm reveals far more midrange information and has superior dynamic range. Bill disagrees, and adds that John evidently can't distinguish bright midrange hash from true detail. He claims that the high-mass arm sounds far more pure, lucid and transparent.

After the beer bottles have stopped flying, they make up by concluding that John prefers his sound "up front" while Bill favors a "laid back" sound.

high mass vs low mass

Who was right? Both were, but not necessarily because of a difference in taste. The higher-mass arm would have produced a smoother sound in both systems (due to resonance absorption and superior rigidity) but it would also have contributed to the output of far more subsonic rubbish. In John's system those subsonics resulted in excessive woofer excursion (back-and-forth movement of the cone), and in a two-way system that would have caused excessive Doppler distortion, audible all the way to the 2 or 3 kHz crossover point...hence the comment about the muddy midrange lacking in detail. The subwoofer would have weeded that out in Bill's system, allowing the benefits of rigidity and low resonance to become more audible.

There are many other variables that could have caused the arms to see-saw in and out of favor. The infrasonic trash could easily induce low-powered amps into overload, making the low-mass arm preferable. Or speakers and/or cartridges with an aggressive midrange might make the high-mass arm more palatable.

The move toward high-compliance (softly-sprung) moving-magnet cartridges in the late 60's and early 70's encouraged the development of mainly low-mass limited-rigidity arms. As moving-coil cartridges gained in popularity, high-mass arms became more common. Today's manufacturers seem intent on developing designs that enjoy the benefits of both extremes, and several new models bear investigation for the innovative technology they employ.

The phono pickup
by Gerard Rejskind

If it doesn't happen here, it doesn't happen at all. The record company has cut into the vinyl of your disc a wavy groove that is mechanically analogous to the original electrical music signal — hence the name "analog recording." By following this groove, the stylus will transmit the mechanical movement to the electrical circuit inside the phono pickup. If all of this happens perfectly, the electrical signal produced by the cartridge will be identical to the original electrical signal that was fed into the record cutting lathe. *If* it all happens perfectly...

But of course that is unlikely, perfection not being of this world, and perfection not being the primary goal of most manufacturers. As you'll recall, many of them are seeking Good Numbers, not good sound.

And as we shall see, pickup makers are as ready as turntable manufacturers to use sleight of hand to make a product seem to be good...on paper.

What's inside a phono pickup? A tiny electrical motor...only it's hooked up backwards.

In a motor, you run an electrical current through a coil suspended in a magnetic field, and either the coil or the magnet will move — whichever one isn't nailed down. In a phono pickup (as in a microphone) the principle is reversed. You move a coil and a magnet in relation to one another, and an electrical current will flow through the coil. Once again, you can either move the coil through the field of the magnet, or you can move the magnet next to the coil. The effect is the same...almost.

In most pickups it's the magnet that moves, because as we shall see that is by far the more convenient way of arranging things. The magnet is placed on one end of a lever called the cantilever...which has the stylus on the other end. The cantilever is suspended somehow, often by going through a rubbery material. So moving the stylus moves the cantilever, which in turn wiggles the magnet. That movement induces a tiny but detectable alternating current in the coil. That current will be (we hope) an analog of the shape of the groove, which is (perhaps) in turn an analog of the original music signal. There is a lot that can go wrong here, obviously. And one thing can go wrong that is *not* so obvious.

The obvious things really *are* obvious. Can the stylus follow the groove properly in the first place, or will it take disastrous shortcuts, generating distortion, losing information, and perhaps even chipping a bit of vinyl in the process? Will the mechanical energy be linearly transferred — which is to say, will the voltage produced be perfectly proportional to the movement of the stylus? Will all sounds be reproduced at the correct level regardless of their

inside the pickup

moving magnet pickups

frequencies? Will other sounds not in the original groove be produced? And will the whole system resonate at some crucial frequency?

Resonances, as we shall see, are at the heart of two major problems, one at low frequency, the other at high frequency.

lower resonance

The cantilever of a phono pickup is springy, rather like the suspension arm on an automobile. You can actually see it flexing back and forth as it rides over the record. It has a natural frequency of resonance, just as the pendulum of a clock does. That exact resonance depends partly upon the springiness of the cantilever: a flexible cantilever will have a lower frequency, while a stiff one will have a higher resonant frequency. It all depends on the mass of the cartridge body itself, and of the tone arm. The greater the mass, the lower the frequency. That is why it is important to match the pickup to the arm: there is an ideal frequency for that resonance. It should be around 12 Hz, where there are no signals to excite it, to "get it going." That ideal frequency is higher than the low-pitched signal from a warped recording...typically around 8 Hz or lower. It is also much lower than any sound that is likely to be recorded on a disc.

too low a
resonance

What happens if that resonance is wrong? An arm/pickup combination with very low resonance may sound fine with a perfectly flat record, but will be unable to play warped records. The pickup will flex down in the valley of the warped disc, and then launch into orbit on the crest. On the other hand if the resonance is very high, as it was with certain extremely low-mass tone arms popular a few years ago, and resonance is excited not by the warp but by the low-pitched sounds on the record itself. The result is a very "tight" and disembodied bass, which sounds impressive at first, but which is ultimately unnatural, and veils the music.

the other
resonance

But the high frequency resonance is worse yet. This is the resonance of the magnetic circuit itself, including the cantilever. It is high in frequency, often higher than the upper limit of human hearing. And it can make a mess of the music. The manufacturers know this of course, but they don't always work to prevent it. Indeed, they use it deliberately, to give Good Numbers…at the expense of sound.

The problem is the presence of the coil in the cartridge. Most pickups are of the "moving magnet" type, which is to say that the magnet is placed at the end of the cantilever, whereas the coil is fixed. You don't want the cantilever weighed down by a huge chunk of metal, so the magnet will have to be small. But that's no problem, because the coil doesn't have to move, and it can be made huge. And it is.

But there's an electrical problem.

does it really
reproduce highs?

A coil can be thought of as a resistor whose resistance changes with frequency. At low frequency it has low resistance — or low *impedance,* as it is called in this context. And as frequency goes up so does its impedance. The coil acts, therefore, like a frequency-dependent resistor placed in the lead from the pickup to the preamplifier. Because there is also a load resistor across the pickup, the two together will act like a filter, cutting off high frequencies. If you are familiar with Ohm's Law, you can calculate this will little problem. Suffice it to say that most moving-magnet pickups behave as though they had built-in filters rolling off everything above 8 to 10 kHz.

Now you may find this incredible, because you've looked at specification sheets, and the manufacturers claim that response extends to 20 kHz or more, not to a mere 8 kHz. Well…that's right. But you are being fooled.

Remember the cantilever's high-frequency resonance. By the way you build the structure of the pickup, you can make that resonance whatever you want it to be. Now if it just "happened" to be an octave above the electrical rolloff point, it would seem to "bring up" the whole frequency response curve, and counteract the droop. If the pickup droops beyond 8 kHz, you make the cantilever resonate at 16 kHz. Problem solved.

Well...not *quite* solved. This trick does for hi-fi what steroids do for athletes. The pickup does not *really* have normal high-frequency response. Resonant structures are handy places to store energy temporarily. So the resonant cantilever absorbs extra high-frequency energy from the record, and then releases it with a slight delay, so that it "adds" to what the pickup itself recovers. This works perfectly on steady-state tones like the ones used in most magazine tests, but of course it cannot deal adequately with changing signals. Like music.

smeared music

What this scheme does in fact is *smear* the music, the way you smear your writing by passing your hand over the page before the ink dries. It destroys stereo information, and loses the subtle auditory clues to the nature of the original room. The timbre of the instruments is altered. Such a pickup does not sound natural, and it cannot reproduce music naturally.

At one time all moving-magnet pickups shared this flaw, and the only alternative was a different sort of device, called — you guessed it — the *moving coil* pickup.

moving coil pickups

The MC pickup (its short name) works just like an MM pickup, only with its major elements interchanged. The magnet is fixed in place, while the coil is wound around the end of the cantilever. Now the magnet can be made huge, whereas the coil will be kept small. A small coil will have negligible impedance even at higher frequencies, and so it can have very wide frequency response. Since the cantilever resonance is not needed to "bring up" the top end, it can be made high enough to be harmless...typically around 65 kHz.

So why aren't all cartridges made with moving coils?

MC pickup problems

Well, there are a couple of drawbacks. If the stylus wears out you can't just pull the cantilever out of the pickup body to change it, because you'd break the little wires connected to the coil. This means you have to send the cartridge back to the factory or some other service centre for major surgery. The other problem is that the tiny coil, which has very little wire in it, has a very low impedance which doesn't match a normal preamplifier input well. What this means is that the pickup has an exceptionally low output, perhaps a tenth of what your amplifier is expecting. Plug it into most amplifiers, and you'll barely hear the music over the noise.

boosting the signal

The signal needs fattening, and there are two ways of doing it. One is with a transformer, which will at once increase the impedance and the voltage. The other is with an extra stage of amplification...called a *pre-preamplifier*. There are advantages and disadvantages to both, as we'll see when we come to the chapter on amplification.

high output pickups

There are also special MC pickups, called "high-output" types. The coil is made larger, using very fine wire, and there is just enough voltage coming out to keep a normal amplifier happy. Of course the cantilever is not quite so happy with the extra mass. And a larger coil means a higher impedance, which gets us right back to the original problem.

Fortunately there are some good moving-magnet pickups on the market. They're not cheap, but they work nearly as well as MC models. They depend on small but exceptionally powerful rare-earth magnets, strong enough to allow the designer to reduce the coil size. The small coil allows reasonably natural response, perhaps to 18 kHz, without artificial boost. The cantilever resonance is then allowed to rise to a harmless 35 kHz or so.

How can you tell a good pickup from a bad one?

Not by its price, though the good ones will certainly cost money. Sometimes the clue is right there in the specification sheet. If an MM pickup boasts very wide response (to 25 kHz, say) it is almost certainly getting it through steroids. The coil inductance may be specified — anything above 0.3 Henries is trouble. And now and then the cantilever resonance may be specified. If it is below 30 kHz, it is storing energy at audible frequencies.

Economy systems can't use good pickups, of course, and that will severely limit their quality. Most systems will do fine with a good moving magnet pickup, which can cost (in Canada) from $300 to $600. Moving-coil pickups (which are not all good either) start around $250 and rise into the thousands. There is little point in making that investment unless your turntable and tone arm are outstanding. And of course an MC pickup will not deliver its promise if you plug it into a second-rate transformer or pre-preamp. There too, price is no guarantee of even reasonable quality.

Installing a pickup

To yield its full performance, a phono pickup needs to be perfectly adjusted, and that means the arm must be correctly adjusted as well. Generally we suggest leaving such adjustments to your dealer, but we have to be realistic. Not everyone has access to a good dealer. Indeed some people who live far from traffic jams and smog have dealers who think a turntable is something you put in a microwave oven to make the cheeseburger cook evenly.

If you want to check the state of adjustment of your pickup, we'll try to help.

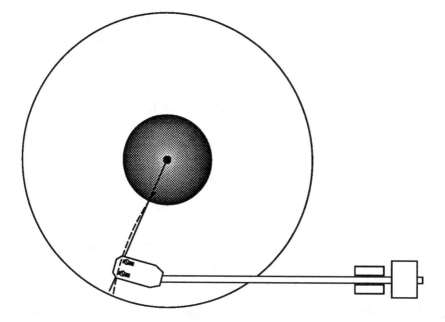

What should happen

An arc instead of a tangent line

Ideally, as the arm sweeps across the record, the stylus point should follow the radius of the record, and therefore always remain perpendicular to it. In fact that's impossible. Though some companies *do* make "tangential" arms which can follow the record radius perfectly, most arms are pivoted. The stylus describes an arc, which is a curve, not a straight line.

If you look at the drawing on this page, you'll see the problem. At best the pickup will be at the correct angle at two points on the record, namely the points where the arc intersects the radius. Anywhere else it will be wrong. Some of the factors determining that angle will already be predetermined: the length of the arm, the angle of its "bend," and its distance from the turntable pivot. What needs to be adjusted now is the exact position of the pickup in the arm headshell. For this purpose most arms have slots to accomodate the mounting screws, so that the cartridge can slide back and forth. It may even be possible to twist it a little, therefore changing the effective angle of the arm. If the arm designer is conversant with mathematics you shouldn't have to do this, but unfortunately some arms are made by people who were off with mononucleosis the day the prof covered the work of J. Baerwald.

how to align a cartridge

Oh yes...Baerwald. His paper on tone arm geometry was published in 1941, which means designers have had half a century to look it up at the library. For our purposes there is one aspect of that paper we need to know. In order to minimize tracking error on a standard long-playing record, the pickup should be adjusted so that it is exactly right at two specific distances: 6.6 cm from the turntable pivot, and 12.1 cm from the pivot. A properly-designed alignment gauge will have alignment marks at *exactly* those distances from the centre.

not all gauges are good

Caution: some gauges are made by people who think they know better than Baerwald. They don't. Before using any gauge, use a precision ruler to make sure that the alignment marks are in the right place.

If you have no gauge of your own, and you can't find one, we've included one in Appendix B, at the back of this book. Cut it out, and glue it carefully to a sheet of thin cardboard with a glue stick, such as the Uhu or Pritt. Cut out the black hole so that the turntable pivot can fit it. Begin with a pin prick *exactly* in the centre, and then enlarge it carefully with objects of increasing diameter (first a nail, then a Philips screwdriver, for instance). Then use a pin to make a dimple at the *exact* centre of each of the other two holes.

Caution: if you photocopy the gauge, use a precision ruler to check that the distances are still correct on the copy. Some variable enlargement photocopiers cannot make exact-size copies even when they are set for 100% magnification. A wrong gauge is of no use at all.

Place the gauge on your turntable, making sure that the pivot is precisely in the centre of the black circle. Then lower the arm onto the gauge so that the stylus point drops exactly onto the inner dimple. To do this you will probably need a flashlight, and you will have to rotate the platter to the appropriate position. You may then want to use a folded sheet of paper under the platter to prevent it from moving, to avoid the possibility of damaging the stylus.

Once the stylus is in place, check the angle of the cartridge body. It should be perpendicular to the radius line, and *exactly* parallel to the ten alignment lines. If it is, proceed to the next step. If it is not, you need to get it right. Initially you should do that by moving the cartridge either forward or back in the arm, *not* by twisting it. Loosen the screws, move the cartridge, and tighten them once more. You will now have to rotate the platter slightly so that the stylus can once more drop onto the dimple. Is it parallel? Repeat the procedure until it is *exactly* right.

Then repeat the test with the outer mark, moving the platter slightly so that the stylus reaches the dimple. Is the cartridge body *perfectly* parallel to the alignment lines? If so your work is done. If not, adjust the position once again so that it is right. Of course it may then be wrong for the inner mark, and you'll have to go back and check.

this could take a while

You may get the right alignment in five minutes, or you may have to repeat the procedure numerous times. If you find that correct alignment is impossible with the cartridge straight, then your arm was manufactured (or at least mounted) by someone who flunked geometry. Twist the cartridge in the mount, if need be, and repeat the procedures until alignment is perfect.

Note that it is difficult to tighten the screws without altering the setting. When we have a setting that is close to right, we like to tighten one of the two screws a lot, so that it can be slightly loosened to allow the cartridge to slide. Once all is right, tighten up the screw that is already fairly tight, and then carefully tighten the other. Recheck the alignment to make sure you haven't moved the cartridge during this operation.

make it tight

And make sure they really *are* tight. We recommend using precision stainless steel screws, not the cheap screws that come with many pickups (some of them are plastic, believe it or not).

vertical tracking angle

Unfortunately that is not the only adjustment which needs to be made, though you might think so by reading the instructions that come with most arms and cartridges. We have adjusted the lateral tracking angle, but we must also adjust the *vertical* tracking angle. This, unfortunately, cannot be done with a gauge, though, incredibly enough, we know of at least one arm which *comes* with a gauge for this purpose (it should be discarded). Vertical tracking angle refers to the forward or backward tilt of the cartridge as it rides on the record. This angle is nearly always altered by changing the height of the tone arm. Some arms allow easy alteration of height, and we know of two arms which actually allow changing the angle while the record is playing! Some arms, on the other hand, have fixed heights, and are not suitable for high fidelity use. *Check this when you are buying.*

Some cartridge instructions tell you to adjust the arm height so that the cartridge body is exactly parallel to the surface of the record. This is almost certainly wrong, as we shall see.

The chisel which cuts the groove into the record lacquer is not precisely vertical. Canting it forward slightly creates less vibration and allows more room for the lacquer chip to be expelled behind the chisel. The industry standard calls for the chisel to be canted forward by 15°. For that reason, cartridge makers are supposed to tilt the electrical elements forward by the same angle. Hence the advice about putting the cartridge parallel to the record surface.

no real standard

But in fact no one seems to follow the industry standard. Records are typically cut, not at 15°, but at 21° or even at 23°. Few cartridges are really at 15° either. It would be nice if there were a true standard, but there isn't. Unfortunately this isn't some minor adjustment that has only a marginal effect on the sound. Vertical tracking angle can *completely change the balance of the music*. A large percentage of audiophiles are dissatisfied with their systems because their vertical tracking angle is wrong. It's a pity that even some high-end dealers don't know about this.

losing focus

An error will be most harmful with a very good cartridge, whose profiled stylus reads the entire groove wall, not just one point on each side. Let us say that the cartridge is not canted forward enough — as often it will not be. In relation to the information in the groove, the stylus will in fact be canted *backward*. Thus the top of the stylus will be reading the recent past, while the tip will be reading the near future. You will hear sound which is a mixture of past, present and future: smeared and unfocused.

But that isn't all. A cartridge canted too far back (if the arm is too low) will sound not only unfocused but too bassy as well. The sound may seem attractively mellow, but it will be blurred and lacking in top end detail. If the cartridge is canted too far forward (if the arm is too high) the sound will be screechy, with glassy, exaggerated highs. Focus will still be poor, and the stereo image will be indistinct. If you get the height exactly right, the focus will be optimum, and the tonal balance will be right as well.

Unfortunately, because records are not all cut at the same angle, the arm should, ideally, be adjusted for each record. With most arms this is hardly practical, and it is necessary to live with a small error on certain discs. Large errors, however, can make even an expensive turntable unlistenable.

record mats and vertical angle

By the way, beware of record mats. Some stores sell expensive replacement record mats which are supposed to absorb vibrations, or do other wonderful things. Because such mats are usually quite thick, they do one other thing: they change the vertical tracking angle. Raising the record is exactly like lowering the tone arm. So a new mat may seem to tame the screechiness of the sound, and yield better focus...when actually the same result could have been obtained by lowering the tone arm slightly. Don't try a new mat without adjusting the arm height.

one final adjustment

We have one other depressing piece of news, by the way: a large change in tone arm height will alter the distance between the pivots of the arm and the turntable. That means you'll have to get out the gauge once more and adjust the lateral tracking angle. Sorry. Now you know why dealers insist on selling quality turntables at full list price.

The Compact Disc

As this book goes to press, the Compact Disc nears its tenth birthday. It has grown both quickly and slowly. At first it looked as though it might die out as quickly as it had appeared. However the disc was backed by two companies that had the financial muscle to overcome all obstacles: *Philips* and *Sony*. The way CD was promoted has been both an advantage and a disadvantage.

how CD grew

In its first years, CD's were difficult to manufacture, and so they were expensive to buy. As the technical problems were overcome the manufacturing costs fell below those of the LP, but *the price remained high*. The high price provided funds for heavy promotion of the CD medium, and it also gave everyone — record companies, artists and stores — a reason to push CD at the expense of LP and cassette. At the same time the high price chased away buyers. The result was that CD became firmly established among those who buy the most records, but at the same time the percentage of homes with CD players grew slowly. At the time this book was written it remained astonishingly small, probably just over ten percent.

the audiophile backlash

As CD became a mainstream medium, there was a backlash among audiophiles, who noticed that the CD didn't sound quite right compared to very good analog (LP) systems. But that backlash barely slowed down the CD. Audiophiles are a small portion of the population. And the new scarcity of vinyl records frightened some of them into biting the bullet, and buying CD players. Fortunately, a number of high-end audio companies began making much better CD players, able to wring a maximum of quality from the discs. And the discs improved as well.

We are not anti-CD, but we are anti-lying. There

Chapter 3: The Compact Disc

are two common lies about CD: (a) All CD players sound alike, because they're all perfect, and (b) All CD players sound alike, because they're all terrible. In fact there are huge differences among CD players. The cheapest ones, inevitably, are just terrible. As we shall see in this chapter, digital audio is a difficult medium, and a lot of companies don't know what they're doing.

Let us begin with an evaluation of the digital medium itself.

Why all digital systems don't sound alike
by Paul Bergman

Ever since the first professional digital recordings emerged there has been a raging debate on the merits of digital versus analog. It was once purely an industry debate, kept from the public as much as possible. It broke into the open only once consumers were offered the Compact Disc player. Even so, consumers who do not read the specialized press may not know there is even a question about the quality of digital sound. But there is, and even digital's biggest boosters (*Philips* and *Sony)* have been forced to acknowledge it. These two companies initially launched CD players with "perfect" sound, but then were forced to improve them...

nothing wrong with digital

Let me say right off that I don't share some of the more fanciful objections to digital sound reproduction. I don't object to having Beethoven or Corey Hart "cut into little binary slices and then reconstituted like frozen orange juice." I have doubts about "scientific" experiments showing that subjects who listen to digital music undergo more stress than subjects who listen to analog music. I also doubt that even an expert can tell by ear, reliably, whether music is coming from analog tape or from a CD. I have, in short, no axe to grind, and my only preference is for what sounds best.

The questions are many. Is digital sound as ersatz as instant coffee, or is it the way of the future? Should we do all our recording digitally to favor the production of quality Compact Discs, or should we call a halt to it right now? Should you buy a CD player, or a high quality analog turntable? I believe there are good arguments on both sides. First let's quickly review how digital recording (tape or CD) works.

how sampling works

A sampling circuit is set up to check, at regular intervals, the voltage of the incoming signal. Professional recorders use approximately 50 kHz sampling, so a sample of the voltage is taken every 0.00002 second. The CD system operates at a slightly lower rate, 44.1 kHz.

At the start of the recording, let us say the voltage is zero. After 0.00002 second it is +1.23 volts. After a further 0.00002 second it is +2.045 volts. Another circuit turns these decimal (base ten) numbers into binary numbers (made up exclusively of ones and zeros) because that's the only sort of number computers can understand. The analog music signal itself will not be preserved. Only the numbers will make it onto the tape, and they will carry just two pieces of information: the time, and the voltage reading at that time.

playing back the data

The playback circuitry will use those two pieces of information to reconstitute an approximation of the original signal. The binary numbers will be reconverted to an analog value, which will then control the output of an amplifier. After this, the signal is once again a conventional analog voltage, capable of being amplified and reproduced by conventional equipment. A bit of smoothing is done so that the waveform doesn't jump suddenly from one value to the next. This is done by a high frequency rolloff filter, either a conventional analog filter, or — in the latest CD players — a digital filter. The digital one is cheaper by the way. This illustration shows the way an audio waveform might emerge from the digital circuits.

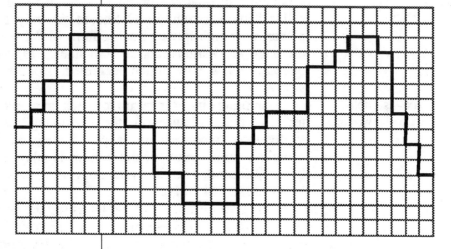

After the filter removes the frequencies above the audio range, the sharp steps in the waveform get smoothed out, and the waveform now looks like this.

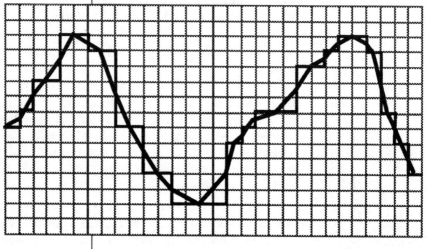

Now this procedure is not an ideal one, because no method is ideal, but it is so different from all traditional recording methods that it neatly sidesteps several traditional problems. Since all frequencies are read in the same way, frequency response can be ruler-flat. Distortion is low, since you can't distort a number. Indeed the reproduction might be perfect except for one small problem.

insufficient
definition

The problem is that the circuits don't keep very good track of what is going on. Bear in mind that samples are taken only every 0.00002 second, and anything that happens between two samples will be missed. What's more, the voltage readings are just as coarse as the time readings. This is because the system has a limited number of digits to play with, and it is forced to round values off. Sixteen digits may sound like a lot, but one of the 16 is used for a parity check (a test to let the error correction circuit know if there's something that needs correcting), and so there are only 15. What's more, remember that the circuits count in binary numbers, not in decimal. Binary numbers take up a lot of space, as you'll see from this little table of equivalents:

Decimal	Binary
0	0
1	1
2	10
3	11
4	100
5	101
6	110
7	111
8	1000
9	1001
10	1010

It's easy to see how quickly binary numbers mount up. When you can count only ones and zeros you get into long numbers rather quickly, so 15 bits isn't really very much. If you were looking at a waveform on a graph, the rounding off would cause errors in the vertical direction (amplitude). The low sampling rate would cause errors in the horizontal direction (time).

Now let me repeat that I am not arguing against the actual method of recording itself. Given a high enough sampling rate and sufficient bits to work with, I don't see why a digital recording system couldn't reproduce music virtually perfectly. The principle is fine. The issue is whether the circuits commonly available today can do the job, and indeed whether the advantages of the new technology are those that are being heralded.

digital misunderstandings

As you may have gathered I think they are not. My impression is that the people who write the actual words you see in spec sheets and ads don't understand either digital or analog recording. For that reason they both overestimate and underestimate the new technology. Let's consider some current claims for digital technology.

CLAIM: *Digital sound is essentially perfect.*

FACT: We heard this claim when the first Compact Disc players came out. In fact all manufacturers have greatly improved their players (improving on perfection?), and even the strongest advocates of CD now acknowledge that not all players sound the same.

CLAIM: *Digital recordings have far greater dynamic range than any analog recording.*

FACT: That's not true. You might suppose that you can't add noise to a number, but digital systems suffer from what is known as "quantizing noise", an artifact of the analog-to-digital conversion process. If all were perfect that noise would be down where the last binary digit is. The noise figure would then be expressed by the formula:

$$20 \log (2^b - 1)$$

where b is the number of system bits. Most modern systems use 16 bits (but throw one bit away on the parity check), and so:

$$20 \log (2^{15} - 1) = 90.3 \text{ dB}$$

Now a dynamic range over 90 dB is enough to make a recording engineer drool, but don't drool yet. That figure relates to the peak-to-peak value of the audio signal, rather than the usual root mean square voltage value. To convert, you subtract the following from the noise value:

$$20 \log (2 \times \sqrt{2}) = 9.03 \text{ dB}$$

less dynamic range

As you'll notice our dynamic range is now down to about 81 dB. And you cannot really record at that level, because the digital "ceiling" is far harder and more awful than that of analog disc or tape. It would be a good idea to knock another 8 dB off that figure. Total usable dynamic range: 73 dB, even under ideal conditions. This isn't earth-shaking. A good analog recorder (12.5 cm stereo, 76 cm/sec) can boast a dynamic range of some 74 dB. Add Dolby or dbx and there's no comparison. Incidentally, all these figures refer to unweighted noise readings, treating noise of all frequencies equally. Weighting curves are often used by both sides to make the specs look prettier.

CLAIM: *Digital recorders have much flatter frequency response than conventional recorders.*

better frequency response

FACT: That's true. Professional analog recorders can be aligned to a tolerance of 1 dB, but only on one particular reel of tape, and only for a limited time. A digital system, including a Compact Disc, can be permanently aligned to within a tenth of a decibel. This advantage is offset somewhat by the fact that the filtering used in digital record/play systems causes massive phase shift across the band, and this can have negative effects on perceived frequency response.

CLAIM: *Digital systems have zero wow and flutter.*

FACT: True, but so what? Modern analog systems have inaudible speed variation.

CLAIM: *Digital recorders have thirty times the distortion of analog recorders.*

lower distortion?

FACT: That's false. The promoters of digital like to quote total harmonic distortion at absolute maximum level: 3% for analog (because that's the definition of maximum recording level in an analog recorder), and 0.1% for digital. Most music isn't at maximum level, however, and as already noted you can't get too close to maximum digital levels. As level drops, an analog recorder's distortion can plunge to as little as 0.01%, whereas the digital system's distortion will *rise*.

CLAIM: *Digital recordings can be copied again and again without quality loss.*

infinite copying?

FACT: This is one of the most cherished beliefs of digital aficionados, and I certainly wish it were true. It isn't. Each time you re-record and re-play a digital signal a few of the digits that make it up will be lost. Lost data in a computer system is disastrous, and so digital recorders and CD players have special circuits that detect missing or incorrect numbers, and make educated guesses as to what those numbers must have been. Some circuits are better educated than others, of course, but even the best of them adds noise and distortion. Each re-recording loses a few more digits, and adds some more guessing.

Now this would be true even under ideal conditions: if all audio accessories (mixing consoles, equalizers, processors, limiters, etc.) were digital. In fact most are still analog (or at least communicate with the outside world in analog fashion), and so each pass requires another digital-to-analog conversion and then a reconversion. Each time some more quantizing noise is added. Further problems are introduced when a signal is dubbed between two incompatible systems: for instance, a *Sony* 24-track digital recorder and a Compact Disc system. The two have different sampling rates, and of course the signal is reconverted to analog to make the trip.

CLAIM: *The newest CD players have much improved anti-aliasing filters, and don't cause the massive phase shift of older anti-aliasing filters.*

better filters?

FACT: This is a strange claim, and it is of course false. The anti-aliasing filter is used to roll off the inaudible high frequencies of the signal, so that they don't run into the 44.1 kHz sampling signal. It's obvious this must be done during recording, not during playback! As I was saying, many digital devotees are abysmally ignorant of the system they're pushing.

the digital advantage

So much for claims and facts. It is nonetheless true that many people are impressed with digital recording, and with Compact Discs. They can't all be wrong, surely? Since I've somewhat bruised the major claims for digital, aren't there some advantages to the system? Yes indeed. As I've already mentioned, digital recording sidesteps some traditional problems. Even the best analog tape has two flaws you seldom hear mentioned.

The first is *scrape flutter*. As the tape scrapes its way past the tape guides and the heads, the drag of friction produces vibration along the tape's length. This means that, as the tape moves forward, it also simultaneously moves forward and back. This tiny but rapid speed variation doesn't sound like conventional flutter, nor can it be read on a flutter meter. The music gets frequency-modulated, with a result that sounds like intermodulation distortion. The music is veiled, and different sounds tend to blend together. LP's suffer from a comparable phenomenon, by the way, one which *Stylast* stylus lubricant is intended to minimize. In any case this flaw is totally absent from digital media.

Then there's modulation noise. It's called that

48

because you can hear it only when there's "modulation" (signal). It vanishes during silent periods, which makes it difficult to measure. This too is a kind of vibration, caused by a slight variation in distance between the tape heads and the tape coating. It can result from both recorder vibration and a slight unevenness in the tape coating itself. Record a pure tone, and you'll hear modulation noise in the form of a crackle. Some studios now do their mastering on recorders that use double-width tape (12.5 mm for two channels) to minimize modulation noise. Digital machines have no modulation noise.

digital imperfections

They do, however, have some audible flaws of their own. The worst is that the higher frequencies are imprecise and unfocused, because of the limited number of bits and the slow scanning rate. This is not evident to all listeners, since a similar lack of focus is caused by poor recording techniques, to say nothing of flaws in analog pickups, amplifiers, and loudspeakers. However a genuine high fidelity system is one in which these flaws (sometimes called "time dispersive" distortion) are minimized. On such a system, the superiority of a properly made analog recording is clearly audible as more natural sound.

Also, digital recordings do not deal well with very soft sounds, such as those produced by hall ambience. This is because a very low level signal "runs out of digits" and is therefore dropped by the digital circuits. In some cases, digital recordings can be clearly heard to have shorter reverberation times than analog recordings. Currently available digital systems cannot accurately reproduce the sound of a room as captured by a classic stereo microphone pair.

reproducing soft sounds

Of course I did say "currently available." Within a few years more sophisticated circuit chips will be cheaply available, making it no doubt possible to sample sound at 100 kHz, with 18 bit resolution.

Such a system will certainly sound better than any other recording system ever devised.

At that time we may come to regret having frozen the CD standard at 44.1 kHz and 16 bits.

The making of Compact Discs
by Paul Bergman

complexity and perfection

Considering that the Compact Disc standard was established so very quickly, it is a marvel of complexity, and indeed, of perfection. It is, of course, the fruit of many years of diligent work, but that work was ongoing, aimed at producing a digital optical medium in (probably) the 1990's. It was manifestly the recession of the early 80's which created the need for quick realization of the CD, and it was only the collaboration between *Philips* and *Sony* which made it possible. *Philips* itself, in fact, was working on a far inferior 14-bit system, and of course the *Sony* digital recorders of that day were 14-bit recorders. The two companies, buttressed by engineering knowhow from a number of firms, quickly imposed a world standard, through sheer economic power, and despite at least one anti-trust complaint. Once the standard was set, there remained only one problem, and that was making the discs.

a gargantuan task

One might think that the very existence of a standard would have made the final step easy. Unfortunately the difficult part of the task was still ahead. That task was so great that the initial *Philips* license agreement, signed by companies which wanted to make Compact Discs, did not even mention the techniques for making them. Those techniques were not fully developed.

This was not necessarily a fatal problem, of course, since both *Sony* and *Philips* had developed their own mastering systems, and a copy of this mastering system was available if one cared to make the necessary investment. Most did, albeit cautiously, since they suspected that the process might not be quite fully developed (how right they were!). Some did not. *Nimbus,* for instance, developed its own system for less than the *Philips* system cost, and used it to become Britain's largest CD maker. More cautious companies were scarcely better off, as the problems of packing so much information on a small disc became obvious. The reject rate at the *Philips* plant was a closely-guarded secret, but it was rumored to be 80%. Most of the output was used to decorate store windows with pretty discs marked, in mercifully small print, "Reject, cannot be played."

high reject rate

This high reject rate accounted for the very high cost of discs. As for the high cost of the first players, that is explained by the fact that the large-scale integrated (LSI) circuits for the digital/analog conversion did not yet exist. Doing it with discrete transistors or non-specialized chips was extremely costly. Even so, manufacturers actually subsidized their purchase. It is widely believed that the first *Sony* players were sold as much as $1000 below cost. That was a cheap investment, however, because it allowed the CD format to be test marketed before capital was committed to the development and production of complex chips.

coding the data

Ironically, the most difficult part of the task — coding the digital information — was done fastest and best. At first glance the task appears easy enough. With each sample, it is merely necessary to note down (record) the time and the status of the signal. This information can then be read from the disc and used to reconstitute the original waveform. And it would be no more complex than that if the transmission system were perfect. In fact it cannot be counted on. There will be transmission errors, and even entire chunks of information skipped. For that reason, early digital recording systems (demonstrated to the professional recording milieu) were unlistenable. The optical disc was not likely to be better in that respect than magnetic tape, and so a method for correcting errors and replacing missing data had to be devised.

a 15-bit system

To do so, an initial sacrifice was made. Though some critics thought the 16-bit words used for the digital codes were already too short, one of the bits was sacrificed, to act as a checksum. If an even number of the preceding 15 bits are ones, then the checksum will also be one. If an odd number of bits are composed of ones, then the checksum will be zero. It is simple to devise a circuit which will compare the 15-bit word with the checksum for consistency. If the checksum is wrong (which will happen only if there is an odd number of errors), the circuit then knows it must do some correction.

error detection

Generally this is quite simple to do. If you see a series of numbers that run:

4-6-8-10-X-14-16

you will have little trouble in determining that the "X" should have been 12. Similarly, if you see a sum of figures, one of which has been erased, you can easily add up what's left and guess accurately what the missing figure must have been. It is easy to devise an electronic circuit that will make the same guess. If the circuit is well designed, the error will actually vanish. That is to say, the replacement data will be identical to the missing data.

However a missing bit is not very much information. One second of audio contains nearly one and a half million bits, and a glitch of any size, on either a digital tape or a CD, will take out entire words, not just bits. These "burst errors" will cause unacceptable discontinuities in the sound unless they are detected and compensated for. This is where the CD code is so outstanding.

52

To minimize the risk of long burst errors, the CD standard "interleaves" the code: it scatters the information around somewhat. One "word" (made up of 16 bits of information) is scattered over three final "words" in the code on the CD. The process will be reversed on playback to recover the original word. This interleaving actually "propagates" the errors. It's obvious that a burst error caused by a fingermark, a piece of dust or a flaw in the original film will affect three times as many words as it would have otherwise. But because less of each word is damaged, it is actually possible to reconstruct what each word must have been. Not all players do this successfully, but a good player can make such errors virtually inaudible. I might add that the CD's "cross interleaved Reed-Solomon code" is far superior to that used on many older studio digital recorders. Digital Audio Tape uses the same system, and for precisely that reason many European studios are switching to DAT for digital mastering.

when error correction isn't enough

Of course it is perfectly possible for a CD to be in bad enough condition (or to have been poorly enough manufactured) that simply too much of the data has been destroyed. There isn't enough left to reconstruct what must have been there. The early digital recorders I heard made horrendous noises when that occurred. Today's CD players do rather better, but of course missing data is never a good thing. If the data cannot be reconstructed, the player must nonetheless avoid noise bursts. When the circuit does not know what should happen next, it has several choices.

(1) *It can hold the previous value over,* in effect repeating a bit of data. This does not produce a very plausible sound, but it does not cause a sudden discontinuity either.

(2) *It can interpolate.* This is like the example I mentioned earlier, in which the missing number in a

series can be guessed. This will, of course, work only if the neighboring pieces of data are intact. You can't interpolate between two pieces of data you don't have.

(3) *It can set the value to zero,* thus shutting off the sound. This is known as muting, and it is precisely what CD players do when they either find the data irretrievable, or the laser beam loses track of the disc sector. The disc then becomes unplayable. It should be noted, however, that some players will mute on some discs that can be quite well played, though with audible errors, by other players. Proper correction and (if correction is impossible) concealment of errors requires a very sophisticated circuit, as well as a considerable amount of computer-like memory. Both are costly, and are unlikely to be found in low-cost players.

how the disc is made

Let us now move to the disc itself.

I would say that the Compact Disc is a remarkable piece of technology which for a long time strained the ability of many factories to produce it. It is made as it is read — by laser. Indeed the laser which makes the CD is no more powerful than the laser which reads it. It does not cut notches into a disc blank like the death ray in *War Of the Worlds,* as you might suppose. Rather it exposes a sheet of photographic film. Using data from a digital recorder (nearly always a *Sony),* it draws a series of very fine pips with its very precise laser light. The film is developed and then used to make a mold. So far this is conventional. This is exactly the way that the tiny transistors and resistors on a chip are formed.

molding it

The mold which holds, in negative form, the shape of the final CD, is then used to emboss a sheet of aluminum foil. The foil is permanently (one hopes!) laminated between two sheets of molded plastic. And the CD has only to be left to cool before it is placed in its jewel box and shipped.

Of course a great deal can go wrong. A typical CD contains six billion little pips on a surface much smaller than that of a conventional LP. The tiniest flaw in the photographic film used for the master will wipe out entire blocks of information. So will a small fault in the substrate which is made from the film, and so will deformations of the aluminum. These deformations do occur, which can be seen in the form of pinholes when you hold any CD to a strong light. The molding process is problematic too. As with a conventional LP, if the mold and the disc do not pull apart in the right fashion, the result will be unsatisfactory: a noisy LP, or a CD fit only to decorate a store window.

That it does not work better than it does may be unfortunate. That it works at all is a wonder.

The problems of Compact Disc
by Gerard Rejskind

Mass-market companies had long had the theory that the turntables they made at "the twilight of the analog era" were near perfection. Indeed, that was the rationale for the development of the Compact Disc: if record reproduction was as good as it was going to get, further improvement required an entirely new medium.

was the CD really needed?

We know, of course, that these companies were fooling themselves, or at least their customers. The turntables they made (but have mostly dropped, fortunately) recovered only a small portion of the information on an LP, and drowned what it recovered in a sea of noise, vibration, and deliberately-induced resonances. But some people never learn. The same companies made the same error with digital audio. They assumed (or at least claimed) that the early players were the ultimate, and delivered virtually perfect sound. They then "improved on perfection" by introducing ever more perfect new generations of players. They should know by now that they are a long way from perfection, and they should also realize that, as with the analog disc system, the source is the most important link in the chain.

forgetting the basics

Some genuine audiophiles also forgot this principle, sad to say, and accepted uncritically the claims of the large corporations. All CD players do not sound alike. And, whatever the problems of the disc itself, simply getting all the code off the record remains a major problem. In this section we will examine some of those problems in detail.

Audio Problems

Most CD players are built to a price, and you don't need a degree in digital engineering to understand their failings. Their analog circuits are poor enough to ruin everything. So fierce is price competition that saving a few pennies can translate into a major marketing advantage, and so a manufacturer will not use a 50¢ chip where a 20¢ chip will do. Yes, nearly all CD players use integrated audio circuits, and not always the best ones. A number of popular models even use the elderly LM741 operational amplifier. That by itself would spoil the quality of the player, even if everything else were perfect.

slow audio chips

The LM741, and some other chips which resemble it, are very slow, which means their output voltage cannot increase faster than a certain maximum "slew rate," usually less than one volt per microsecond. To give you an idea how slow that is, the TLO84 chip, which is better but still not wonderful, has a slew rate of 13 V/μs.

What happens if the input signal requires a faster increase than this? The output signal increases at its natural slew rate instead of following the input signal (see illustration on the next page). The result is "transient intermodulation distortion," often abbreviated TIM or TID. Curiously, some large

tions cannot possibly be audible.

And in all fairness slew rate limitations should matter less with CD than with analog audio, because the CD's frequency response is brutally chopped beyond a frequency of 20 kHz. Even so, let us examine a "worst case" scenario: a full-level 20 kHz signal that goes to the limit of the circuit's dynamic range, which typically might be 7 volts rms. The entire cycle of the signal takes place in 1/20,000th of a second, which is 50 microseconds. The signal must increase from zero to maximum level in a quarter of that time, however, in 12.5 μs. The peak value of 7 V rms is 7 x √2 = 9.90. If the signal increases from 0 to 9.9 volts in 12.5 μs, then simple division indicates that the circuit must have a slew rate of at least 0.792 V/μs. The LM741, however, has a specified slew rate of only 0.3 V/μs.

Those who don't believe in TIM object that the problem will occur only at ultrasonic frequencies

Ideally the side of this square wave should rise perfectly vertically...

...but the output voltage cannot rise faster than the circuit's speed allows

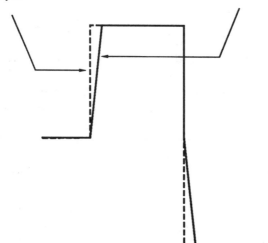

Those who don't believe in TIM object that the problem will occur only at ultrasonic frequencies anyway, and that it will not be heard, because it will sound like a filter which merely rolls off inaudible frequencies. TIM is audible in fact, because it is not simply harmonic distortion, adding inaudible spurious harmonics to the sound. It is intermodulation distortion, whose products can be detected in the audible band.

the weakness of
the preamplifier

But that is not the only problem of the audio circuits in CD players. A CD player contains an entire preamplifier every bit as complex as a phono preamplifier. When you consider the problems of phono preamps, and the cost of a truly good preamp, you can well imagine the quality of preamp to be found in a $600 CD player.

And remember, these are plain, ordinary analog audio problems, the ones that should be the easiest to fix. We haven't yet touched the much thornier question of getting the code off the disc.

Mechanical and Optical Problems

the impossible
task?

To get an idea of what the CD player is up against, try examining the playing side of a Compact Disc with the 30X microscope typically used to examine phono stylus tips. You won't be able to see the tiny little "pits" which make up the signal. The distance between these pits is as small as the wavelength of visible light, small enough to "bend" the light by diffraction. That's the reason for the CD's famous "rainbow" effect.

through the
microscope

Now if you have a good lab microscope you really can see the little pits, but your player must be able to "see" them without the quality optics of that microscope. Indeed nearly all CD players use plastic lenses little better than those used in disposable cameras. As the disc spins by at speeds that reach some 3600 rpm, a lot of information can get lost.

58

following the digital
track

sensitivity to
vibration

This situation is made worse by the fact that the "digital" information is actually recorded in analog form. The information on a typical CD requires six billion bits (binary digits). There isn't room on the tiny disc for six billion little indentations, and so a simpler scheme is used. A single indentation has a length which is proportional to the value of the entire 16-bit "word," which means that we can get by with "only" 370 million of them. However the player then has a much more difficult job to do. It is not merely checking to see whether a number should be a one or a zero, it must accurately evaluate the length of each of the 370 million indentations, and it must do so with a plastic lens on a disc which is spinning at the speed of a power saw! No wonder the CD system requires a sophisticated error-correction system!

Indeed, many CD players have trouble even following the track...and if you listen to FM radio you'll know they often fail. In some players there is not one but three laser beams, with two of them surveying the "groove" and keeping the main laser on track. To make the corrections, an electronic "servo" system is used, which notes when the laser gets lost and gets it back where it should be. Naturally the servo system can act only once there is mistracking, and in the meantime, with data coming in at the rate of 1.4 million bits per second, there will be a lot for the error-correction circuits to do.

Once you understand these problems, it is easy to see why CD players are as sensitive to vibration as analog turntables are. The task of code recovery is difficult enough if the mechanism is perfectly stable, well-aligned, and vibration-free. If in fact it is mechanically no better than a power tool (and in low-cost units it cannot be), the task becomes all but impossible.

Peek inside the average CD player. That's

right...the frame of the mechanism is made of plastic!

Digital Problems

It is well known that the worst problem of early CD players (and the cheapest ones today) was caused by the low-pass filter. The filter was unavoidable. After all the CD contains signal up to a frequency of 20 kHz, and the digital sampling circuits were operating a little more than an octave higher, at 44.1 kHz. The two had to be kept apart, and so a sharp "brick wall" filter simply chopped the audio. Like all filters, this one introduced a phase error, which means that it delayed the passage of certain audible frequencies relative to others. It also "rang" electronically, causing serious problems. Modern machines use "oversampling" of at least four times. Note that this adds nothing whatever to the resolution of the system, since the extra samples are redundant: each piece of data is simply repeated four times. However this allows the sampling circuits to operate at a higher frequency, namely 176.4 kHz, and the filter can be much gentler. Note that one player actually uses 16 times oversampling, a figure so high it can get by with no filter at all.

a different wasy to make CD's

Note that a similar filter is used in the making of the Compact Disc, and that filter cannot be omitted. One CD maker, *Chesky*, claims to get better sound through "64 times oversampling." We don't know what "oversampling" means in the context of recording, and David Chesky just smiled when we asked him.

Just as some players use higher sampling rates than the disc, some also use circuits with more bits. It is currently in fashion in mass-market advertising to boast of 18-bit or even 20-bit circuits. The words on the disc are recorded with 16 bits, which means that the signal level at any given moment is expressed by a number composed of 16 binary digits (1's and 0's). Certainly if these higher-bit circuits had existed in 1981 when the CD was being designed, digital audio could today be a lot better than it is, but you cannot add digits that are not there. So what's the point?

why more than 16 bits

To understand why it is done, take an 8-digit scientific calculator, and ask it for the value of π. It will probably give you a result of 3.1415926. But can you be sure of that last digit? Perhaps it should have been rounded up to 7 rather than 6. The only way to be sure is to know the ninth digit. If you check a reference book, you will see that the ninth digit of π is 5. Thus the eighth digit *should* have been rounded up, and π should therefore be expressed as 3.1415927.

For the same reason it can be useful to use an 18-bit circuit to read a 16-bit number. The extra bits help get the final digit right.

extra bits are not enough

However in most players this matters very little. The poor player struggles frantically to evaluate the length of a piece of data through a plastic lens, and if it can get it to within 14 bits it is doing well. Unless the mechanism and optics are of extraordinary quality, the extra bits will simply be invented by the circuit, and will be only incidentally related to the value recorded on the disc.

aligning the player

There is an additional problem in most players: that of alignment for the "least significant bit." When the level gets down very low, the circuit will reach the last bit: that bit will be either a one or a zero, but it cannot be in between. A well-aligned digital circuit will be neutral, favoring neither one nor the other. Unfortunately alignment requires expensive manpower, and most CD player are built for customers who are not very demanding except on selling price. And so typically the alignment will not even be done. If there even is an alignment potentiometer, it will simply be placed in the middle of its range. The resulting error can easily be seen on an oscilloscope, by looking at a sine wave tone recorded at, say, -60 dB. The wave will be distorted, or — worse — it will oscillate between a sine wave and a distorted wave! Note that this represents a serious flaw: an oscilloscope is not a very sensitive distortion meter. Distortion can be heard long before it can be seen.

can it be done better?

What is To Be Done?

If you were designing a state-of-the-art CD player, what would you do? Well, you would probably design a mechanism with finely-machined parts and vibration-free bearings, like those on an analog turntable. You would make as many parts as possible of cast metal for maximum rigidity. You would use an optical system of laboratory quality. You would use digital circuits adjusted for true 16-bit resolution. And you would add a preamplifier section worthy of a top-grade high fidelity system.

Last but not least, you would attach a price tag to the finished unit. It's easy to figure out that the price would not be low. Bear this in mind as you read reviews of CD players. The designers of these devices have done the best they can, but they are not magicians.

Buying a CD player

getting access to the whole repertoire

Should you buy a CD player?

Probably. As we write, anyone who wants access to the entire musical repertoire must have both a turntable and a CD player. There are recordings that are not available on LP. And some material on LP will never be transferred to CD. You need both.

How much you should spend on each depends on how you will be listening. If the CD player will be largely used for background music, you can safely buy a moderately-priced player, one that may not thrill you, but that at least won't annoy you. If it will become your main music source, on the other hand, get the best one you can. If it means settling for cheaper electronics and loudspeakers, so be it. With digital as with analog, the source comes first.

the first impression

Initially even moderately-priced CD players sound seductive. There is a startling clarity about the sound, and it's a relief to hear that clear sound emerge from silky silence. Of course if that impression were to last, there would be no problem.

the second impression

But for most people it doesn't last. The "clarity" turns into an annoying brightness after a few hours, or even a few minutes. In fact a great deal of musical detail is missing. In particular there is less sense of depth, less of a feeling that the music is coming from a three-dimensional space, that the musicians are not merely painted on the wall. Instruments with quite different timbres sound strangely alike. You hear all the sounds, but you don't hear the music.

With the cheapest players, those with the "brick wall" filters to keep the audio and the sampling signals apart, there is more: a total lack of focus in the highs. It is as though you were listening through a crack in the door.

The best CD players sound nearly like analog sources, but without analog flaws. They have depth and a good stereo image. The highs sound natural and pleasing even after you've been listening for a while.

don't buy from just anyone

Now here's a suggestion that may sound radical. Buy your CD player from a store that also sells good analog turntables. Buy it from a store that can sell you genuine high fidelity. But it from someone who can convince you of its quality, not with figures and specifications sheets, but with a musical demonstration that leaves you wanting more.

The difference between a good player and a

mediocre one may jump out at you, but don't count on it. Be prepared to listen for a long time. And if you don't like what you hear, don't let *anyone* tell you the player is good.

Not the sales clerk.

Not even us.

"NO WONDER IT SOUNDED SO MUTED. THE AMP WASN'T GETTING ENOUGH POWER!"

Amplifiers

Ask your friends what an amplifier does and you'll get a lot of strange answers, if not simply blank looks. There is so much mumbo-jumbo to be found in amplifier ads and magazine "test reports" that even many audiophiles are confused about the role of the amplifier. Certainly there are not many who could explain rationally why there are amplifiers, preamplifiers and pre-preamplifiers...and why some sources need preamplifiers while others apparently don't. At best they could list the order in which these devices are hooked up (pre-preamp, preamp, then amp) and identify the preamp as being "the box with the knobs on it."

what an amplifier
does

The main job of an amplifier is to take a small signal and make it bigger. The second — and more visible — role is to allow you to control what signal you listen to, and what happens to that signal.

The signal from virtually any music source — microphone, vinyl disc, Compact Disc, cassette, video — is very tiny, perhaps a thousandth of a volt or so, sometimes less. Such signals are fragile, because they are not much bigger than interfering signals from the environment: hum from the house wiring, "hash" from the furnace fan, or even radio signals all around us. For that reason it is urgent to fatten them up a bit, so they can be manipulated safely without getting mixed with noise. The device which does this is generally called a *preamplifier*. It amplifies the voltage of the signal by something in the order of a thousand times...which means that from the original two millivolts it may have been, it will come out at two volts. From there on the *power amplifier* takes over, and amplifies the signal further, so that it contains enough energy to move the speaker cone, and therefore the air in the room.

The preamplifier
by Paul Bergman

There is nothing in a preamplifier which inherently costs a lot of money. And indeed it is possible to purchase a serviceable phono preamplifier for a very small amount of money, as a glance through a *Radio Shack* catalog will show. A basic preamplifier for a magnetic cartridge, without volume control, costs only $29.95 (catalog No.42-2109). When you consider that *Radio Shack* does not operate on the smallest of markups, it is easy to see that there isn't much to a basic preamplifier.

build your own preamp?

Indeed you can build your own. Below is the diagram of a preamplifier using a TLO84 integrated circuit. An experienced builder can put together a working preamp in an evening, and still find time to watch the late TV news. That preamp is not precisely what I would call high fidelity, but you might be surprised how many expensive preamplifiers use the same chip.

However this does not mean that expensive preamplifiers are mere packaging, intended to cheat you. The fact is that the basic circuit found in low-cost units ("low cost" includes integrated amplifiers

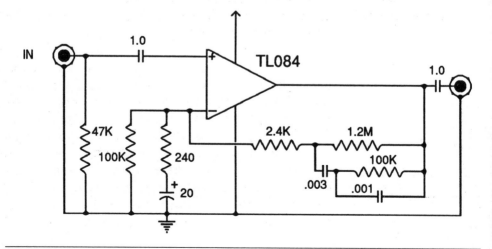

with prices of as much as a thousand dollars) have several problems which affect the sound you hear.

why preamps are expensive

One of them has to do with the configuration of the input stage, which consists of one or more transistors (or — to be open-minded — tubes). Typically, there is a feedback loop around that stage. That is, a sample of the stage's output is brought back to the input and mixed in out of phase, so that it cancels rather than adds: hence the name, *inverse* feedback. Feedback can have three effects. First, since cancellation is taking place, the gain, or amplification, of the stage will be lower. This means this stage, or an amplifying stage which follows will need more gain in order to make up for it. Secondly, the signal that is fed back will contain a small amount of distortion, and as it is reinserted it will actually cancel some of the distortion at the output. Third, the feedback loop may alter the frequency response of the stage. This may be done deliberately, by including a filter within it, so that there is more feedback (and therefore less amplification) at some frequencies than others. This is exactly what has been done in the integrated circuit preamplifier whose diagram is shown on the page opposite.

problems of feedback loops

The feedback loop presents two problems, however, and both are serious enough to lead some designers away from this configuration.

The first has to do with speed. From my description of the way feedback works, you can see that the loop shapes the frequency response so that it corresponds to the RIAA response curve needed to play back analog records. It should be evident, however, that a signal which has already reached the output of the amplifying stage cannot possibly be corrected by whatever happens back at the input. It follows that, for a short period of time after a change in signal, the signal cannot be corrected by the feedback loop. For that instant the amplifier will be operating in an

68

"open-loop condition," as though the feedback loop were disconnected.

This sounds rather worse than it is. "A short period of time" does not mean half a minute, or even half a second, but nor can it be entirely neglected. Electrons flow at approximately the speed of light — fast enough to circle the globe seven times in one second — but an amplifier is far slower. If it is slow enough that it cannot keep up with the increase, it will suffer from *slew distortion*. In the case of a preamplifier which is equalized by a feedback loop, the start of a fast signal will be unequalized, which means that it will sound much too bright.

another problem

The second problem of the feedback loop concerns loading of the input. If you look at my preamplifier diagram, you will see that there is a 47,000 ohm resistor between the input and ground. Such a resistor is standard for all moving-magnet cartridges. However the feedback loop is also connected to the input (a different input, which inverts the phase of the signal...but the two inputs meet inside the chip). Because of that feedback loop, the input of the preamplifier will "look" to the phono cartridge not like a pure resistance, but like a *reactance*: an impedance which varies with frequency. Since the coils inside the cartridge are also reactive, behaving like frequency-dependent resistors, the effective impedance of the circuit will vary a great deal with frequency. Frequency response will be far from flat, and the circuit will probably "ring" (resonate) at several frequencies.

yet another problem

In some preamplifiers, indeed, there is one more problem yet. Remember that the circuit must have high gain in the bass, and much less gain in the treble. For that reason, at high frequency it will have a great deal of inverse feedback applied to it, in order to lower its gain. At low frequency it will have much less, and it may not in fact have any at all. If the circuit has not been designed for very high performance even under open-loop conditions, it will of course suffer from excessive distortion in the bass.

Incidentally, though I have been discussing these problems in terms of phono preamplifiers, you should understand that you are not immune from them if you use some musical source other than a turntable. CD players and cassette decks have preamplifiers too, and they also contain frequency equalizing circuits. The problems are precisely the same.

You may know that high-end hi-fi designers, in contrast to the designers of "professional" equipment, use as few parts as they possibly can in building their equipment. This is especially important with a preamplifier, because the signals can be less than a thousandth of a volt, and they are fragile. Extra controls and switches — especially tone controls — add many components without improving the sound. Switch contacts are especially treacherous: they can act like resistors, capacitors, and crystal diodes all at once. The latter effect is little known. Air pollution quickly tarnishes the metal. Impurities at the surface behave much like the impurities that are deliberately introduced into semiconductors, such as transistors and diodes. The "diode" can then act like the detector of a crystal radio, with results that can well be imagined. The best switches, then, are airtight, and the contacts are plated with the only highly conductive material which does not tarnish: gold. Connectors are often gold-plated for the same reason. Switch contacts will need to be under considerable pressure, which means they may be hard to turn.

Even more troublesome than switches are volume and balance controls. It is already difficult enough to make resistors which are stable and noise free, but a variable resistor presents additional problems, since

not just turntables

keeping equipment simple

troublesome controls

it is in a sense both resistor and switch. Imagine a long resistor, with a sliding contact which must press against it without suffering from the problems I've already mentioned. Ordinary volume controls use a carbon rod, or even simply a carbon track bonded to plastic. More expensive controls use what is sometimes called "conductive plastic," which is a moulded track of hard plastic mixed with conductive substances. This material is tougher, and can tolerate much higher contact pressure, and for that reason it is likely to be stabler and more reliable. Conductive plastic is used in most modern studio mixing consoles, by the way. At one time a rather better (but more expensive) scheme was used: a rotary switch with many contacts, with fixed resistors connected to them. These switched attenuators were more reliable, since it was possible to have a gold-flashed slider against gold contacts under pressure. Some high-end designers may wish to pick up the idea.

choosing transistors with care

You may have gathered, however, that the transistors used can make a difference to the sound. I have certainly suggested that an integrated circuit chip like the one shown in this chapter, has no place in a high fidelity product. It is known that particular transistors have a "sound" of their own, a fact seldom found in printed specifications sheets. However designers like to select transistors for certain characteristics. For example, some transistors are designed to have particularly low noise. To lower noise further, they can be run at relatively low voltage. The difficulty is that a low voltage circuit will overload easily. Certainly a circuit whose RIAA equalization comes after the first stage, which must face the unequalized signal, will overload very easily. Designers may then compromise: high voltage on the transistors, and never mind the noise. Makers of mass-market preamplifiers are more likely to choose low voltage in order to get low noise, because the noise figure is commonly included in the spec sheets.

Some of our largest manufacturers are convinced that designing a preamplifier is a matter of simply knowing basic electronics. It is much, much more.

The pre-preamplifier
by Gerard Rejskind

At the start of this chapter we said that a signal may arrive at the preamp with a voltage as low as two-thousandth of a volt. In fact it can be a lot less than that. Some advanced audiophiles use phono cartridges known as *moving coil* cartridges, "MC" for short. The reason for this is covered in another chapter, but the important aspect of the MC pickup is its very low voltage output. Instead of 0.002 volt, it may have an output of a mere 0.0002 volt. Needless to say, it will require special treatment.

how to amplify a very small signal

That treatment can take different forms. Some preamplifiers (or preamp sections of integrated amplifiers) have a switch to raise the "gain," the amount of amplification. Some preamplifiers actually have an extra stage of amplification to get the extra gain. That section is called, as you've probably guessed, the *pre-preamplifier*. And sometimes the pre-preamp is a separate unit, which can be purchased separately.

MC transformers

(There are two other solutions. Some preamplifiers have interchangeable modules, which are optimized for either conventional or MC pickups. It is also possible to increase the voltage by using a transformer. This is quite an attractive solution, since transformers, unlike amplifiers, do not produce noise. Quality MC transformers are extremely expensive, however.)

Separate pre-preamps are becoming a rarity, even among high-end audio freaks. They are inherently expensive, since they come in their own boxes with their own power supplies. They also require extra output jacks and cords, which can only make the sound worse. Today most pre-preamps are tucked inside the preamp itself.

Power amplifiers

This is the final link in the electronic chain, the black box (and that's usually what it looks like) that takes the moderately large signal (typically 2 volts at extremely low power) and amplifies it to many watts, enough to move the cone of a loudspeaker. At first glance the power amplifier is straightforward: it takes a signal and makes it bigger, nothing more. There are no controls (it is out of fashion for power amps to have more than on-off switches), and there is no need for equalization or signal switching, as there is in a preamplifier. You would think power amplifiers could be made nearly perfect, and that therefore they would sound virtually the same.

do all amplifiers
sound alike?

Indeed many people outside the hi-fi world believe that to be the case. Some years back, in a double blind test at the National Research Council, subjects could not reliably tell one amplifier from the other. Since the head of the project, physicist Dr. Floyd Toole, is associated with a well-known Canadian mid-fi magazine, that magazine was quick to trumpet the conclusion that "all amplifiers sound alike." A large US mid-fi magazine also happily spread the news...happily because that is what it had been saying all along.

what the test really
means

But of course the NRC test *doesn't* indicate that all amplifiers sound alike, merely that people couldn't tell them apart *under those particular test conditions*. Serious flaws in other components, notably music sources, can mask deficiencies in amplifiers. Use the typical mass-market turntable or CD player, and you will probably be hard put to tell the difference among amplifiers. But if the system is of

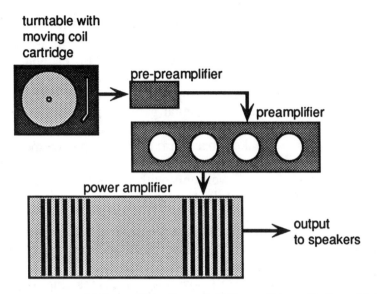

turntable with
moving coil
cartridge

pre-preamplifier

preamplifier

power amplifier

output
to speakers

high quality, there is little problem distinguishing.

(In case anyone asks...yes, we have done blind comparisons of amplifiers, not only with our own group, but with neophytes, who could not see the brand names, and wouldn't have recognized them if they had. We have yet to find *anyone* who couldn't hear a difference, or who even thought the difference was insignificant).

Do we know *why* amplifiers sound different? In some cases no, in other cases yes. The same designers who can't seem to master the design of preamps and tone arms also — surprise, surprise! — have a lot of problems with power amp fundamentals. Several blunders are common:

how not to build an
amplifier

(a) *The high feedback amplifier*. Paul Bergman mentioned feedback a few pages back, in the discussion of preamplifiers. A sample of the output is brought back to the input, where it is introduced out of phase (electrically reversed) so that it cancels some of the amplifier's gain, and also cancels some of its harmonic distortion. High feedback is popular, because so many manufacturers are hung up on distortion figures: a figure of 0.00005% looks *so* good on a spec sheet, and it gives the mid-fi salesman who is striving to be heard over the cacophony of the TV sets something to talk about. Unfortunately feedback makes an amplifier *slow,* and it's easy to figure out why. The signal gets to the output uncorrected, and it is only when the contents of the feedback loop make it back through the amp once more that correction occurs. It is obvious that such an amplifier will work well only with signals that change slowly over time. Like test tones.

another blunder

(b) *The high damping factor amplifier.* The damping factor is a measure of an amplifier's ability to control the cone of the speaker, and of course that is a good thing.

Here's how it works. As the amplifier signal flows through the speaker's voice coil, the speaker acts like a linear (back and forth) electric motor, and the cone moves. But at the same time the speaker also acts like an electrical generator, and it generates a "back voltage" which it sends back to the amplifier. *If* the amplifier has a very low internal impedance, it will virtually short out that back voltage. That will tend to brake the cone motion, and the cone will be less likely to go on flapping after the end of the signal which set it in motion.

Most power amplifiers do in fact have low impedances. If an amp has an internal impedance of 0.2 ohm and the speaker has an impedance of 8 ohms, the damping factor will be:

$$8 \div 0.2 = 40$$

This is a typical value, but some amplifiers have damping factors of 80 or more. You might suppose that a higher figure is better, but in fact it makes little difference. A glance at the diagram opposite reveals why.

As you can see, there is more than the amplifier's

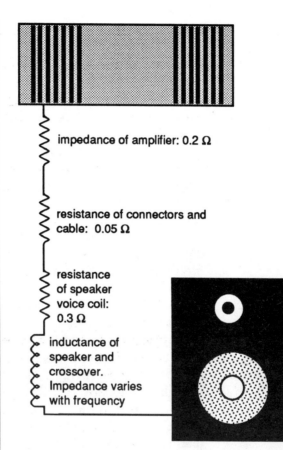

impedance of amplifier: 0.2 Ω

resistance of connectors and cable: 0.05 Ω

resistance of speaker voice coil: 0.3 Ω

inductance of speaker and crossover. Impedance varies with frequency

own impedance between it and the speaker. There is also the electrical resistance of the connectors and the cables, the impedance of the elements in the speaker's crossover network, and the impedance of the many turns of fine wire in the speaker voice coil. Simply reducing *one* of those elements — the amplifier impedance — won't improve real-life damping.

why a very big damping factor is a bad sign

This might be a harmless little delusion, except for one thing. The usual method of achieving a high damping factor is by the use of heavy feedback. There's nothing harmless about *that*. We suggest avoiding amplifiers with damping factors much higher than 40.

limiting frequency response

(c) *The wide bandwidth amplifier.* Is unlimited frequency response a good thing? Some years ago an experiment indicated that if you filtered out frequencies above 20 kHz (which are theoretically inaudible anyway), listeners thought that music lacked liveliness and warmth. That experiment was flawed, it turned out. The filtering was done with the same sort of sharp filter which is now commonly found in CD players, and its phase-shifting effects *in the audible band* were clearly detectable. On the other hand, unlimited high frequency response is not an unalloyed blessing. Some music sources, particularly analog, contain inaudible signals and noises of extremely high frequency. If the amplifier is not "fast" enough to keep up with the signal, then something unpleasant will happen. Each sound wave, instead of increasing at its natural rate, will increase at the maximum rate the amplifier can manage. The result is what is known as *transient intermodulation distortion* (usually abbreviated either TIM or TID). Even though it happens far above the range of human hearing, some of the distortion products are right out where you can hear them. By the way, since high feedback amps are relatively slow, they are most vulnerable to TIM. And — wouldn't you know it! — those are the very amps that are built with frequency response "from DC to light."

a really bad amplifier

(d) *The amplifier with the notch.* The first transistor amplifiers sounded different from tube amps, and many audiophiles didn't like them. But mid-fi salesmen (the only sort there was back then) insisted that the new amps were virtually perfect. Brandishing spec sheets showing very low distortion, they said that we "just weren't used to hearing sound of such purity." (The same argument would later be used to defend the flawed sound of early CD players).

In fact those first transistor amplifiers suffered

from a curious problem. Distortion was indeed very low *at full power,* but as power dropped, distortion increased. From a fraction of one percent, it climbed to nearly 10% at low level. No wonder the amplifier didn't sound right!

What was wrong? In the "push-pull" designs which were (and are) used in power amplifier output stages, one transistor (or set of transistors) amplified the positive half of the signal, and another amplified the negative half. The problem came at the "zero crossing" point, when one transistor handed off to the other. There was a small "notch," a discontinuity, which was clearly visible on an oscilloscope (and in the illustration above). It had a negligeable effect on full power signals (which is what most lab tests are made with), but because the notch was fixed, it became more important as level dropped.

bad designs never die

Now and then we still find expensive amplifiers with notch distortion. If you check amplifier harmonic distortion graphs in mid-fi magazines, you'll see that some amplifiers have distortion that increases at low power. Those amplifiers have notch distortion, though the magazines will never tell you that. After all, all amplifiers sound alike, don't they? A test at the NRC...

not enough current

(e) *The starving amplifier*. A power amplifier cannot put more electricity into the speaker than it can obtain from the electrical power supply. But good power supplies (the part of the amplifier that turns 110 volts alternating current into the direct current the amplifier can use) require heavy transformers and large capacitors, both of which are expensive. And since those don't contribute to improving the published specifications, the power supply is a good place to cut if you're a mid-fi manufacturer. The amplifier *might* be good if it weren't so starved for power.

unstable circuits

(f) *The unstable amplifier*. Remember the description of how inverse feedback works? The key word is *inverse*. The feedback signal must be a mirror image of the input signal: it must be positive when the input signal is negative and vice versa. Otherwise the gain will increase instead of decreasing, and the amplifier will oscillate, possibly destroying the speakers.

Well, no one ever gets *that* wrong. However some poorly-designed amplifiers contain "phase shift," an alteration of the timing of the signal, with the result that, at some frequencies, the feedback signal is no longer *exactly* opposite in phase to the input signal. Few such amplifiers will actually break into full blown oscillation, but they may suffer from the *beginning* of oscillation. They will ring electrically, just as a bell rings mechanically. At such frequencies distortion will be very high.

Some amplifiers are marginally stable. One sample may have reasonably acceptable performance, and another may ring horrendously. Even the two channels of the same amplifier may not sound alike.

(g) *The non-linear amplifier*. There is a principle

sacred to the best amplifier designers: first make an amp which sounds good with no feedback applied at all. And then improve it with feedback.

ignoring the basics

Some younger designers have never heard of this principle, or if they have they think they know better. Some have hatched "clever" new designs, in which the amplifier puts out, not sound, but a series of electrical pulses which are controlled by the input signal. If you fed this highly non-linear signal to a speaker, it would sound horrible. However, large amounts of inverse feedback are used to make this signal linear once more. *What is wrong with this picture?*

So much for blunders. Let's look at other ways to run amplifiers, ways which lead to something other than sonic disaster.

Class A

class B for efficiency

Remember the description of notch distortion, and the explanation of how complementary transistors handle the positive and negative halves of the signal? Industrial amplifiers operate in what is known as class B: during the positive half of a cycle, the negative transistor shuts down and waits until it is needed again. That's highly efficient, and efficiency is what you want in most applications.

class AB for the best compromise

However most hi-fi amplifiers operate in class AB. Each transistor continues to operate during a part of the cycle when it could be relaxing. That enables it to do a more graceful handoff to the other transistor, and avoid notch distortion. Class AB amplifiers run a little hotter than efficient class B amps, but not much.

finally, class A

The class A amp throws away all notions of efficiency. All the output transistors are switched on *all the time*. There can't possible be notch distortion, and indeed the distortion pattern of a class A amplifier is different from that of a conventional amplifier.

On the other hand there is a price to be paid. Because the transistors are always switched on, the amplifier is running flat out all the time, even when it isn't putting out sound. It needs a very sturdy power supply, and it needs to dissipate a lot of heat without self-destructing. Class A amplifiers are expensive, needless to say, and the heat they throw off can be a problem in the summer. Because the design constraints are so great, it is difficult to make a high-powered class A amplifier, and most manage outputs of only 25 watts per channel.

Some of the world's best amplifiers operate in class A. However not everyone think class A is a good thing. Some very good designers claim that the advantages of class A are imaginary, and that the high heat of class A has a negative effect on circuit operation.

class A isn't for everyone

Our own view is that class A amplifiers are not for everyone. Fortunately there are some superb class AB amplifiers as well.

a warning

Caution: the mid-fi people have taken notice of the advantages of class A operation, and attempted to make money from it. Several of them have what are purported to be variations on class A, called by names such as "new class A," "super A," etc. The general idea is that the amplifier operates in class A when there is a signal, and it drops down to class B when there isn't a signal. If you've read this section attentively, by now you'll be at least chuckling.

Bridged amplifiers

more power for free?

Can't find a power amplifier as powerful as you want? By a hookup known as *bridging,* a 100 watt per channel amplifier will (sometimes) put out as much as 400 watts. The catch is that the two channels operate as one channel, and you need two stereo amplifiers instead of one.

How do you bridge an amplifier? The amp in

question needs to have an internal circuit which allows it. That circuit reverses the phase to one of the two channels. That is, one channel amplifies the signal while the other channel amplifies its mirror image. You then connect the speaker across the two red terminals of the two channels, ignoring the black terminals completely.

bridged stereo amplifier

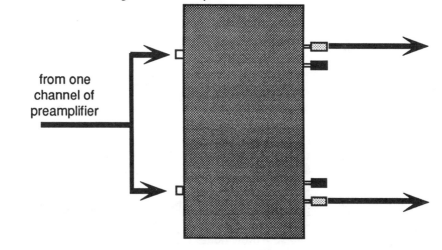

from one
channel of
preamplifier

bridging for
professional sound

Bridging can be useful in professional sound application. If a Pink Floyd concert needs a 2000 watt amplifier, you can get that power by bridging a 500 watt per channel monster amps. However we don't recommend this for high fidelity, because bridging circuits seldom sound transparent. If you need more power, you're better off selling your amplifier and buying a bigger one.

Tube amplifiers
by Paul Bergman

Remember when all amplifiers used tubes? Surprise! Some of them still do! And there are reasons, besides nostalgia, for the survival of the tube in high fidelity amplifiers.

Let us go back in time.

The first tube, a diode, was introduced in 1904, long before the word electronics became widely known. It wasn't an amplifier, but rather a *rectifier,* a device which transformed alternating current into direct current.

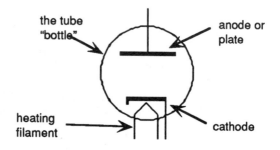

The anode (also called the plate) and the cathode are a certain distance apart inside a metal or glass bottle from which air has been extracted. Normally no current can pass between them, since they aren't connected. However, there is a third element, a *filament,* which heats the cathode enough that electrons begin to boil off into the vacuum. Where do those electrons go? If the plate has a negative voltage on it, they are repelled, since it is as true in electronics as in romance that "opposites attract." But if the plate is positive (as it is during each half-cycle of the alternating current), the electrons are attracted to it, and a current flows across the vacuum. But of course the flow is strictly one way. The diode was literally an electronic valve (and the British still use the word "valve" for the electronic tube).

Then an inventor named Lee De Forest got an idea which would revolutionize communications and make high fidelity possible. He placed a positive DC voltage on the plate so that a continuous current could flow. And then he added a third element between the cathode and the anode: a control grid. If the grid is strongly negative compared to the cathode, the grid will repel the electrons before they can get to the plate, and the current will stop. If the grid is *slightly* negative, a current will flow, but it will be diminished. If the grid is not negative, maximum current will flow. For the first time a weak current (on the grid) could control a much stronger current (flowing from the cathode to the plate). The electronic amplifier was born. De Forest called his invention the *Audion,* though it would later be called the triode.

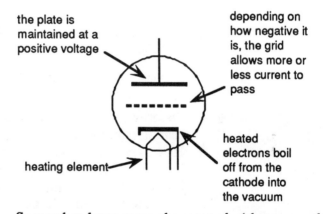

the plate is maintained at a positive voltage

depending on how negative it is, the grid allows more or less current to pass

heating element

heated electrons boil off from the cathode into the vacuum

a more powerful tube

Somewhat later came the *pentode* (shown on the next page), which has three grids. The *screen grid,* placed near the plate, has a positive voltage on it, though not as strong a voltage as that on the plate itself. The screen grid accelerates the flow of electrons by attracting them, and then letting them flow through the grid to the plate. The *suppressor grid* is slightly negative and repels electrons which would otherwise bounce off the plate. The pentode amplifies more than the triode does.

are pentodes hi-fi?

I should, however, mention that the use of pentodes in high fidelity is somewhat controversial, because some people believe that triodes yield less

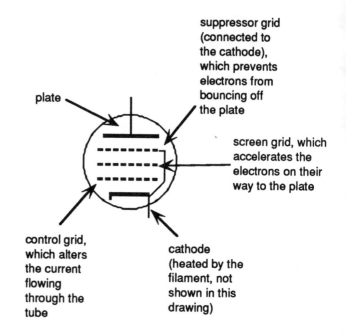

plate

suppressor grid
(connected to
the cathode),
which prevents
electrons from
bouncing off
the plate

screen grid, which
accelerates the
electrons on their
way to the plate

control grid,
which alters
the current
flowing
through the
tube

cathode
(heated by the
filament, not
shown in this
drawing)

distortion. For that reason, some tube amplifier manufacturers boast of their "all triode" designs. However it would be rash to condemn pentodes. If it is possible to use a single pentode instead of two triodes, the result may be superior. The pentode's very high impedance also makes it the device of choice in the driver stage, the part of the power amplifier that precedes the output.

tube disadvantages

Tubes suffer from several disadvantages from which transistors are (largely) immune.

(1) *Very high cost.* Tubes themselves are costly because they are made in small quantities. But even when a 12AX7 dual triode could be purchased for $1.20, a transistor cost only a few cents. Today's integrated circuits make it possible to produce hundreds of transistors for a dollar. It's obvious that electronics could not have become so widespread without the development of transistors and microelectronics.

unreliable

unpredictable

noisy

worse than noisy

too hot

a bad match

(2) *Doubtful reliability.* The tube is a little like a light bulb: it burns out. At one time most pharmacies had tube checking machines. Today most transistors are permanently soldered in place.

(3) *Variable quality.* The characteristics of a tube depend on factors that are difficult to control, such as the exact placement of the elements, the quality of the vacuum (which is never complete) and the temperature. Output tubes are often matched, just as transistors are, but it is relevant to say that the designer of the tube cannot know what his tube is going to be used for.

(4) *High noise.* Early transistors were actually noisier than tubes, but tubes suffer from a noise source that cannot be eliminated: "thermionic noise," caused by collisions of the electrons heated by the filament. Today's transistor amplifiers are many times quieter than tube amplifiers.

(5) *Microphonics.* It is obvious that the slightest movement of the elements in the tube will cause a variation in the current flow. And so even sound waves can change the current. The tube is said to be microphonic. When a highly microphonic tube is placed in a very sensitive preamplifier circuit, it is actually possible to induce acoustic feedback into the system, the same phenomenon you get when a microphone is placed too close to a public address speaker. Some designers claim that transistors can also be microphonic, by the way, but of course the phenomenon is much worse with tubes.

(6) *Heat.* Need I say more? However I should add that heat is not good for transistors either. Heat can shorten the life of a tube, but it can provoke the sudden failure of a transistor.

(7) *Impedance too high for loudspeakers.* Impedance is a difficult concept for non-mathematicians, but it is unavoidable in this case. Power is equal to voltage multiplied by current. If a

circuit has high current and a low voltage, it is said to have low impedance. If it has low current and high voltage, it is is said to have high impedance. Here is the problem. The voice coil of a typical loud-speaker has a low impedance, typically 8 ohms. A tube, on the other hand, is a high impedance device and furnishes voltage more easily than current. In or-der to match tubes to speakers, it is necessary to use a transformer. That seriously limits the usefulness of tubes in audio. We know how difficult it is to build a quality transformer for moving coil phono pickups. An amplifier output transformer must be of the same quality, but must be able to pass millions of times more power.

not powerful
enough

(8) *Limited power.* It is certainly possible to build a 200 watt tube amplifier, but such amplifiers were rare before the advent of the transistor. Some design-ers did place several tubes in parallel in order to ob-tain increased power, but they then had to make their own output transformers. The cost became astronomical.

the advantages

So much for disadvantages. The continued exis-tence of tube amplifiers means that there must be ad-vantages as well.

(1) *High impedance.* I realize that I listed this among the disadvantages, but it has advantages as well. The high impedance of a tube preamplifier is an advantage, because it is less likely to influence the behavior of a phono pickup or a tape playback head.

(2) *High voltage.* Transistors require power sup-ply voltages of 15 to 70 volts, whereas tubes can use voltages of 150 to 450 volts. It is obvious that you cannot obtain an output voltage greater than the sup-ply voltage, and so a transistor amplifier "runs out of breath" more easily than a tube amplifier.

(3) *More graceful overloading.* If you overload a transistor, it becomes progressively less linear,

which means that the output current will no longer be exactly proportional to input current. But at one point, the top of the wave will be "clipped," a phenomenon accompanied by the generation of much harmonic distortion. The tube also becomes non-linear, but it doesn't clip the wave. And so a tube amplifier pushed too hard merely sounds increasingly fuzzy. It is interesting to note that some musicians rather liked this effect. The "fuzz boxes" used by some rock guitarists are intended to simulate the sound of a tube amplifier overloading.

why some people prefer tubes

(4) *Factor X*. There is a "tube sound" which certain audiophiles like. It is characterized by smooth and warm highs (the absence of sudden death overload?) and by richness in the lows (the effect of the output transformer?). There is also factor X: audiophiles sometimes say, "I don't know why, but I like it."

It is obvious that superb amplifiers can be built with transistors, and there are numerous examples. But the tube, for all its disadvantages, is far from dead.

How much power? How much loudness?
by Paul Bergman

It is certainly possible to build a good amplifier of very high power, but it is very difficult. Our favorite power amplifiers are capable of less than 100 watts per channel, with 50 watts being typical. This may not be enough to drive a small, sealed speaker, but today's more efficient speakers can thrive with that sort of power.

it takes more than raw power

However it's important to know that power is only one of the factors affecting how loud you can play music. One amplifier may have exactly the same output as another, but be able to play much louder. There are numerous reasons.

The rules for measuring and specifying amplifier

power are well laid down in law. Since most countries have substantial penalties for not living up to advertised claims, virtually all manufacturers are rather conservative. This means that if an amplifier is rated at 60 watts, you can expect it to put out as much as 70 watts by the official method. This is done so that the worst unit to come from the plant on a Friday afternoon will still pass official tests and keep its maker out of serious trouble. A few small manufacturers still act as though the law did not exist (they also usually do not bother getting *CSA* or *UL* electrical safety approval) but this is a reasonably marginal phenomenon.

Power ratings are important, but it is well known that an amplifier's power rating is only one factor influencing its apparent loudness. The result is that if amplifier A measures the same as amplifier B, it may nonetheless sound much louder. It is my impression that the editors of most magazines prefer to ignore such "unreliable" impressions, whereas more subjectively-oriented audiophiles allow this fact to exacerbate their ever-so-slightly paranoid suspicions of all audio measurements. Thus it may be instructive to consider what factors can be identified that contribute to this subjective loudness difference.

what limits power output

Let us proceed then. There are several limits on the power output of an amplifier circuit:

(a) *Power supply voltage.* The voltage supplied to the output transistors will be, for longevity's sake, at least a little below the prescribed maximum for the transistors used. When the amplifier's output voltage reaches the supply voltage, it can rise no higher. If it attempts to do so, the waveform will be clipped off at the top. A clipped waveform is rich in spurious harmonics that are irritating to the ear.

(b) *Output current.* This too is specified for the transistors used. Going beyond maximum specified current will result in heat build-up in the transistor, causing it to fail. The better the heat sink system of the amplifier, the faster heat will be dissipated into the atmosphere, and the closer one can afford to get to the maximum limits.

(c) *Transconductance curves*. These are curves showing the relation between input voltage and output current for different bias levels of the transistor. It is not my intention to turn this discussion into a tutorial on solid-state design, so suffice it to say that it is essential to operate the transistors over the linear part of their transconductance range, that is, in the range over which output is directly proportional to output. Wandering beyond those limits results in increasing distortion.

slow transistors

(d) *Transistor speed*. This buzz word is misunderstood by many people. A fast transistor is one that can pass a signal very quickly, which is of course necessary if it is to process high-frequency information. On the surface this appears not to be a problem, since all amplifiers seem to have adequate high-frequency response. In fact, however, some amplifiers use low-speed transistors which have inadequate amplification at the high-end. They are made to *seem* adequate by the application of negative feedback — bringing a sample of the output back to the input to correct the amplitude error. This works well in steady-state tests, but there are some circumstances in which amplifiers behave, under normal conditions, as though their feedback loops were disconnected. So speed, sometimes expressed in terms of "open-loop bandwidth" (frequency response with the feedback loop disconnected) is essential. *Note:* this is not to say that an amplifier should have unrestricted high-frequency response. On the contrary, very high-frequency (non-audio) signals may be faster than the speed of the transistors can deal with, and trigger what is called *slewing distortion,* which is audible.

the power supply
is one key

(e) *Available drive current.* Though the output transistors should be the factor limiting how loud the amplifier can play, in fact the earlier amplifier stages will sometimes overload before the output does. This indicates gross carelessness in design, and means that efforts to optimize the operation of the output stage are largely wasted.

(f) *Power supply stability.* Ideally the supply which feeds the output transistors would always maintain the same voltage no matter how much (or how little) current it furnished. This is generally the case only in class A amplifiers, which are designed so that they operate flat out even when they are not producing sound. Class AB amplifiers — the overwhelming majority — require a current supply that will vary hugely over even very short periods of time. As current need increases, nearly any power supply's voltage will drop. Of course the signal going to the speaker will drop too, exactly when it is supposed to increase. The output waveform will be squashed down somewhat, and distorted. This may not sound as harsh as outright overload, but such an amplifier will sound at best somewhat muted.

The solutions to this problem are not inexpensive. A good small amplifier should have a power supply like that of a much larger amplifier, with a high-current transformer, large capacitors, and expensive current chokes (large coils) instead of cheap resistors. The power supply should have a "low impedance," which means that it should look to the amplifier as though it were short-circuited.

Now if it actually *were* short-circuited, no current could flow from it. What is necessary, then, is that it behave like a short-circuit for alternating currents (such as audio) but like a high impedance for the direct current it must supply. This may sound impossible, but in fact a large capacitor has exactly the desired characteristic: it has a very low AC impedance, but an infinite resistance for direct current. With such a large capacitor across the output of the power supply, the amplifier will think it is looking into a short circuit.

Life is not really so simple, unfortunately. At low frequencies, a very large electrolytic capacitor may behave as though it had a small resistor connected in series with it. The power supply no longer looks like a short circuit, and its voltage will change substantially as the current changes, even if the supply contains an electronic voltage regulator. To avoid this highly undesirable effect, a large capacitor may be "bypassed." That is, a smaller capacitor will be connected across it to short out those low-frequency AC signals. Of course, smaller capacitors have higher AC impedance to begin with.

the subjective side

These, then, are some of the factors that determine how loud an amplifier sounds. There are more subjective factors too. Different amplifiers will behave in different ways when they reach their limits. If an amplifier is limited by its power supply current, loud waveforms will be softened, with fairly subtle distortion. The same will be true of an amplifier that is allowed to operate outside the linear part of its transconductance curves: it will sound progressively less musical as the volume rises. However an amplifier that is limited by power supply voltage will clip the top from loud signal waveforms, and will sound terrible. Such an amplifier must be run well below its limits, and the user's impression will be that there isn't very much power to spare.

distortion and loudness

It is also well known that harmonic distortion is perceived by the human ear as loudness, and so an amplifier that distorts will seem louder than one that does not. For this reason it is best to be suspicious of an amplifier that seems to be too loud for its size. An extensive period of listening will reveal whether its virtues are real.

Putting it together: the integrated amplifier
by Gerard Rejskind

Do you need to have the power amplifier, the pre-amplifier, and (perhaps) the pre-preamplifier in separate boxes? No. And most people buy them together in one box. They get what is known as an *integrated amplifier:* everything in one.

But in North America integrated amps have an image problem. They are considered to be compromises, one step above mass-market junk. You get one unless and until you can afford something better, namely separate units.

That reputation is undeserved. There is an obvious advantage to putting everything into the same box: you avoid two sets of jacks and an interconnecting cord. Since it is known that jacks and cables are a source of problems, why aren't *all* amplifiers integrated?

It's a good question. To be sure, with separate units you can keep the sensitive preamplifier circuits well away from the magnetic field of a large power amplifier's power supply. But people who buy separates often stack them together anyway! It's true that with separate units you can upgrade a step at a time, but then separates cost more to start with.

Partly it's snobbism. Having an integrated amplifier means you're not a "real audiophile," just as driving a four-door sedan used to mean you were a dull, unadventurous family-oriented slug, unable to cope with a clutch pedal, or with instruments more informative than idiot lights.

And partly it's self-fulfilling prophecy. Many consumers *expect* integrated amplifiers to be mediocre, and so manufacturers don't bother putting their best circuits into integrated boxes, because they think there's no market. This goes double for receivers, which are integrated amplifiers with AM/FM tuners included. With few exceptions most are horrendous because people *expect* them to be.

Of course there are exceptions. It may be true that the very best amps and preamps come separately, but a few integrateds can outperform most separates. Keep your ears — and your mind — open.

Listening to amplifiers

amplifiers really are different

Considering that all amplifiers are supposed to sound alike, it's amazing how much they can change music. One amplifier will sound shrill and set your teeth on edge. Another will be warm and rich. One amplifier will be open, revealing an exceptionally realistic stereo image. Another will be opaque: when something loud plays, you don't hear anything else.

how to check this out

You can check this out for yourself in a good store, and we recommend you do. But beware of one trap: *loudness*. Mid-fi stores try to sell you very powerful amps, and they demonstrate that, as you turn up the volume, sure enough things get clearer. Beware!

the importance of clarity

Bad amplifiers just don't sound clear. Because you can't hear detail, you keep wanting to turn up the volume to make the sound clearer. It works…for the loud sounds. But music is not made up just of loud noises. Tiny overtones, which give depth and breadth and soul to the music, are soft. A bad amplifier will not reproduce them audibly, no matter how much power it has, or how loud you play it.

"WE DISCOURAGE CUSTOMERS FROM GETTING TOO CLOSE. FINGERPRINTS ARE NOTORIOUS FOR INDUCING RESONANCES!"

Loudspeakers

Loudspeakers look deceptively simple, and no component is more familiar. It is the one most people think of first when they consider upgrading their stereo systems. Conventional wisdom has it that the speaker is the most important part of the system, and that it is the weakest link. This is untrue. The music *source* is the most important part, and it is often the weakest link as well.

But that is only the start of the misconceptions about loudspeakers. There are others, as we shall see. Let us examine the way speakers work first of all, and then we can consider different ways of building high fidelity speakers.

How speakers work
by Paul Bergman

tried and true technology

Most loudspeakers use essentially the same technology. The typical loudspeaker is simply an electric motor designed to move back and forth rather than in circles. The speaker cone (called a diaphragm or a dome on smaller models), being itself moved by the voice coil, must make the air in the room vibrate, to produce what we perceive as sound. I note that audiophile magazines are in the habit of saying that a speaker can "move a lot of air." It is important to understand that this does *not* mean that the speaker is setting up a breeze in the room...unless things are going drastically wrong.

why a speaker needs a cabinet

You might suppose it would be possible, æsthetics aside, to simply hang a single loudspeaker from the ceiling by a wire. In fact there is a reason that cannot work. A loudspeaker has two sides, and at any given moment those two sides are doing opposite things. As the speaker cone moves forward, an observer at the rear of the speaker would see the cone moving backwards. Both sides play music, but the two are out of step with each other. If they are allowed to mix, they will cancel each other out.

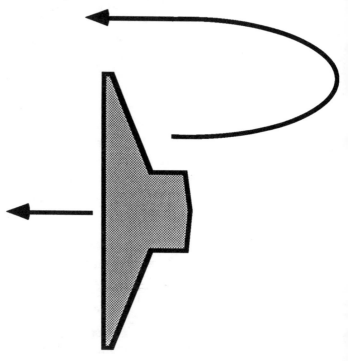

highs and lows travel differently

Actually that is not quite what happens. It is a fact of acoustical life that lower frequencies are omni-directional, going all about the room in all directions, whereas the higher frequencies tend to go in straight lines, not unlike a light beam. For that reason the lower frequencies from the two sides of the speaker will mix more thoroughly than the highs, and they will cancel more efficiently. This is why a naked speaker will sound reedy and thin, with little low-frequency output.

Once you understand this little dilemma, it will occur to you that it would be advantageous if you could simply get rid of the wave coming from the back of the speaker. You could, for instance, cut a hole in the wall and mount the speaker in it, so that only one side would play into the room. This is a perfectly plausible solution, and in fact this solution has a name: the infinite baffle. The harmful "back wave" is "baffled" by the separate space — in this case the outdoors.

inifinite baffles

This is less than practical, of course, though some people in the early days of hi-fi actually used a large closet or even another room in exactly that way. Most of us prefer speakers that have actual cabinets, intended to dispose of the back wave, but without taking up all the living space.

Such speaker systems, if they are large enough, may be still be called infinite baffles, though of course they are scarcely infinite. As monophonic sound gave way to stereo many years ago, most commercial speaker systems shrank considerably, and the very expression "infinite baffle" fell into disuse. Performance problems began to appear. The air trapped in a small enclosure has considerable stiffness, which opposes the movement of the speaker cone. Distortion increases considerably. Because of the stiffness, the resonant frequency of the cone rises. Unfortunately a loudspeaker has little useful output below its own resonant frequency.

And so two new solutions became popular. It seemed obvious that the stiffness problem could be

bass reflex
speakers

relieved by putting an opening in the box. That would allow the back wave to get out, of course, but this could actually turn out to be helpful. The cabinet and the hole (usually called a "port") form a resonant tube. If this tube were to be "tuned" (by adjusting its size) to match the speaker resonance, the tube itself would form what is known as a Helmholtz resonator. You may recall from high school physics that, in such a case, the two ends of the tube will resonate in step; in other words they will be in phase once again. This is the basis of the bass-reflex speaker, sometimes called the tuned-port enclosure. In some variants, a passive driver (an extra woofer, with a cone but no voice coil) is placed over the port so that it can absorb energy at the resonance point.

acoustic
suspension
speakers

The other solution, first popularized in the 1950's by *Acoustic Research*, is even more novel. Because a very small cabinet has such a stiff air mass, and will boost the cone resonance so much, that characteristic can be used to advantage. Build a woofer with a very floppy cone, without the very stiff surround that can be found on most speakers. The cone resonance will be much too low for proper operation of course, so very simply you use the stiffness of the air in the cabinet to support the cone. With that small air space behind it, the cone's resonance will now rise to a reasonable level, and all will be well.

inefficient
speakers

Both of these methods are in common use today, though acoustic suspension speakers are less popular than they were, because they are rather inefficient. For one thing it takes a good deal of energy to fight the stiffness of the air. For another, it is simply getting rid of the back wave rather than using it to reinforce the front wave. The result is that acoustic suspension speakers may require two, or even four times more amplifier power than reflex speakers.

tuned enclosure
disadvantages

For rather a long time reflex speakers were out of favor, because so few manufacturers knew how to tune them properly. Poorly-tuned speakers had serious problems in the lower frequencies, and they were demonstrably inferior to sealed speakers. I would be the last to argue that everyone has now discovered the way to tune a speaker enclosure, but there are now some designers who can do the job as it should be done. These speakers often sound superb. True, there remains a disadvantage that is inherent in this sort of speaker. Below the resonant frequency of the woofer, the cone is not restrained much by the tuned enclosure. The cone will therefore flap quite a lot when it is excited by subsonic material, such as record warp signals. Systems using such speakers should ideally have low-frequency filtering.

wood isn't ideal

Whichever method is selected by the designer, several other problems must be faced. One is that wood, or indeed any material used to build the cabinet, is not totally opaque to sound. This should be evident, but many designers appear not to have thought of it. If this is true of wood, it is surely even more true of the fiber (cardboard) tubes used for the port in the typical reflex speaker. For a portion of the sound, then, the cabinet does not exist. This is especially important at the frequency at which the cabinet sides resonate. At those frequencies, the sides will have little sound-stopping power at all. For those and other reasons, it is necessary to prevent the cabinet from resonating, and it is desirable to use as dense a material as possible. Chipboard, the material most used for loudspeakers, is less than ideal, but of course it is cheap and easy to handle. Some manufacturers use a quite dense wood fiber panel called *Medite,* which is somewhat better, whereas others use ceramic materials. One British manufacturer uses *Aerolam,* an aluminum/honeycomb sandwich originally developed for aircraft. It should be noted, however, that all of these materials have characteristic resonances, and that these may color the sound unless they are used very carefully.

multi-way speakers

The final problem results from the fact that, except in very simple systems, a single speaker cannot adequately reproduce the full range of audible frequencies. It is therefore customary to have a degree of specialization. In two-way systems, favored by many audiophiles, a woofer reproduces the lower frequencies, and a tweeter (which is much smaller) handles the higher frequencies. A crossover network, made up of capacitors and coils, divides the frequencies up so that each band goes to the appropriate speaker. And the designer's problems are only beginning. I shall deal with crossover problems shortly.

phase problems

Obviously it is not possible to have an instantaneous division between the woofer and the tweeter. For that reason, there will be a considerable range of frequencies that will be reproduced by both the woofer and the tweeter. Depending on the distance from each driver to the listener's ear, the two waves may either reinforce each other or cancel each other out. In practice, as one moves out from the axis, one's ear will move, in alternation, from reinforcement zones to cancellation zones. This is sometimes called the *comb filter effect,* because the resulting frequency response curve, were we so brave as to plot it, would resemble the teeth of a comb. Ideally the woofer and the tweeter should be made to share the same space, but of course this is not possible.

This is by no means an exhaustive list of the problems in designing a high fidelity loudspeakers, but it is certainly enough to keep a designer busy for months, even years. It seems to me that some designers, bent on reinventing the wheel, often trip up on these very basics. They then spend their time on fine-tuning — anti-diffraction grilles, high-quality internal wiring, and gold connectors — when they might better study the basics. We might then have fewer loudspeakers in the marketplace, but it seems certain that we would have more good music.

Crossover networks
by Paul Bergman

If plenty of things can go wrong with the design of a loudspeaker system (and they usually do!), the trickiest thing to execute properly is the design of the crossover network. Crossover design has actually become a sub-specialty of audio engineering.

passive crossovers

I should tell you that most crossover engineers I've met are very fond of the passive crossovers used in nearly all loudspeaker systems. This is, I think, a professional bias caused by the realization that if there were no passive crossovers, they would find themselves unemployed. I find their enthusiasm rather too optimistic. Most of the larger recording studios I know use three-way speaker systems with an electronic crossover and a separate amplifier for each driver. If cost is no object there are good reasons for doing it that way.

I'll acknowledge, however, that some crossover engineers are very good at their jobs, and that their best creations sound nearly transparent, almost as though they weren't there. This is all too rare, unfortunately.

Let's start by describing what an ideal crossover network should do. It should roll off unwanted frequencies quickly, but smoothly and predictably. It should introduce no "phase shift," which means that sounds from the different drivers remain in perfect step. It should have the same input impedance at all frequencies. It should not store electrical energy. It should not waste any of the amplifier's output. Finally it's input-to-output impedance should be zero at all frequencies.

If you've been very, very good, Santa might bring you such a crossover next Christmas. It's sure that no speaker manufacturer ever will.

Crossovers, whether they're simple or complex, are made from two basic building blocks: inductors and capacitors. It's easy to get them. Any electronic parts stores sells "non-polarized" electrolytic capacitors (ones that work both ways, with no positive and negative terminals), and they often sell ready-made crossover coils as well. You can also buy magnet wire and wind your own coils if you have a little patience.

To understand how a crossover works, look at the very simple ones in this illustration. They are first-order Butterworth crossovers, using series construction in the first case, parallel construction in the second.

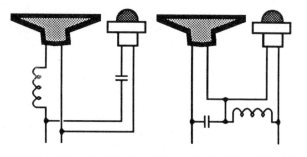

inductors and capacitors

You can think of an inductor (the coil) as a resistor whose value varies with frequency. At low frequency it has low resistance (called "impedance" in this case), and as frequency rises so does its impedance. A capacitor is also a frequency-dependent resistor, but it works the other way, conveniently enough: it lets high frequencies through more readily than lows. So look at the crossover on the left. At low frequencies the coil will act almost like a piece of straight wire, letting sound into the woofer, whereas the capacitor will act like a resistor, keeping the signal out of the tweeter. At high frequencies they will work the other way around. The crossover on the right is an alternative hookup, in which the coil and capacitor short out the drivers at the appropriate frequencies.

first order crossovers

This setup works quite well, and in fact some manufacturers actually use crossovers no more complex than that. There is a serious drawback to such "first order" crossovers, however. Their effect is rather gradual. Beyond the crossover point, response falls by a mere 6 dB/octave. If it begins rolling off the signal to the tweeter at a frequency of 4 kHz, say, the signal will be reduced only 6 dB at 2 kHz, 12 dB at 1 kHz, and 18 dB at 500 Hz. Unless the tweeter can handle prodigious amounts of midrange (and even upper bass!) signal, it may well distort or even burn out. The crossover can be set higher, of course, but then it is the woofer which will have a disproportionate amount of work to do, and it may be no happier about it than the tweeter.

Butterworth filters

A word about terminology before we push on. Mr. S. Butterworth is the engineer who, some fifty years ago, described the filter that bears his name. Virtually *all* crossovers use Butterworth filters, because they are the only ones that don't cause ripples in the frequency response around the crossover point. The term "first order" refers to the fact that there is only a single "pole" or filter element. A second-order crossover is in effect a stack of two filters, and rolloff takes place at 12 dB per octave. Again there are two ways of doing it.

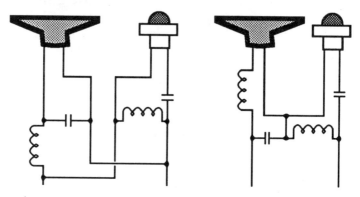

higher order filters

In fact it is rather common to use higher-order filters, despite their complexity and therefore their cost. The only alternative is to use drivers which are, to all intents and purposes, wide-range reproducers. This isn't ideal. The woofer and the enclosure in a two-way system will then have to be optimized for performance rather far up the band, perhaps as far up as 8 kHz. This is not terribly compatible with making it perform well in the deep bass.

choosing a crossover design

I must admit that this is not what I am used to working with, even when my monitors have passive crossovers. Monitor builders, even the dimmest ones, give priority to broad frequency response, because studio producers insist on it. They will not normally be awed by the thought of spending a few extra dollars on capacitors and coils. For that reason they will not use first-order crossovers. Such crossovers are usually found in speakers from audiophile-oriented makers trying to provide quality on a budget. That is because first-order crossovers offer an additional advantage I haven't mentioned yet: *good phase response.*

Though this is the major topic I intended to tackle in this section, I must confess that I'm not sure how to do it without losing at least 90% of my readers. There's a lot of mathematics in this, and the sheer length of the equations is forbidding. The editor asked me to keep it…well, non-technical and accessible. Easy to say! In any case if your math is still fresh, you may either know the equations or know where you can find them.

So let me try this tack. The two sorts of elements used in crossovers introduce *time distortion*. The reason will be evident if you consider how they work. A capacitor is essentially two large plates which are parallel but do not touch. As electrons flow toward one plate, an electrical charge builds up on it, which (because electrons repeal each other) chases the electrons away from the opposite plate. Once they're gone all current stops, of course. Because we're dealing with currents which alternate in direction, however, the source of electrons will soon reverse and the process will occur the other way. Capacitors store electrical charge, please note, and for that reason they delay the signal.

So do inductors, of course. Since they are in effect alternating-current electromagnets, they store energy in the form of magnetism.

You can probably already anticipate what must happen. Different frequencies will be *shifted in phase* (i.e. in time) so that they will no longer be in step when they emerge from the speaker. Some designers are fond of quoting a rather ancient study demonstrating that the human ear is insensitive to phase errors. I consider this study's conclusions to be highly debatable at best, but it is in any case irrelevant. Your ear might or might not notice a time delay between a tone of 200 Hz and another of 8 kHz. That is *not* the phase problem you'll get in a typical loudspeaker, however. You'll hear a phase shift

time distortion

phase shift

between a 2 kHz tone emerging from the woofer and *the very same tone* emerging from the tweeter!

It's impossible to overestimate the seriousness of this problem. It's often described in terms of disturbance to the frequency response, but that isn't the half of it. Phase shift between drivers sounds like *distortion,* not just poor frequency response. It's a horror. An excellent singer will sound as though she's suffering from impacted wisdom teeth, and that ain't high fidelity.

simple crossovers: good and bad

First-order crossovers are tolerable in this respect, as I've already indicated, but there's one important way in which they're worse. Because their rolloff is so gradual, the band of frequencies shared by both the woofer and the tweeter is very large. So whatever phase error is present will be noticeable over much of the audible bandwidth.

third order filters

That is why better loudspeakers usually use third-order crossovers (with rolloffs of 18 dB/octave). Of course using more elements actually increases phase shift, as you might suppose, but in this case that is an advantage. At the crossover point the phase shift will actually increase to 180°. This means the drivers will behave as though one of them had been connected backwards. The designer will then *actually* connect it backwards, and all will be well.

Or *almost* all. In fact all will be well only at one frequency, but because the "handoff" from one driver to the other is so rapid, the problem band is relatively narrow.

what about second order filters?

At this point you may be wondering about second-order crossovers. How do you get the drivers in phase using one of these? In fact you don't, and using filters of an even order is (in my view) a major error frequently committed by crossover designers. Some designers try to get their drivers back in step by offsetting them physically. The speaker that is "ahead" (usually the tweeter) is placed farther back

---

Chapter 5: Loudspeakers

so that its wave will take slightly longer to arrive, and then it can get back into step.

This solutions works at only one frequency, of course, and a second-order crossover (which cuts at only 12 dB/octave) allows plenty of bandwidth for anomalies to call attention to themselves.

why use second order filters?

It is only fair to add one thing: some designers have good reason to use second order crossovers. A woofer or tweeter, when it reaches the limits of its frequency response, will roll off the signal at a rate of 6 dB/octave. This mechanical limit acts just like a first order crossover network. A second order electrical crossover plus a first order mechanical crossover is equivalent to a third order network.

three-way systems

Many loudspeakers are three-way systems, and their complexity is quite daunting. Here's a typical third-order three-way crossover.

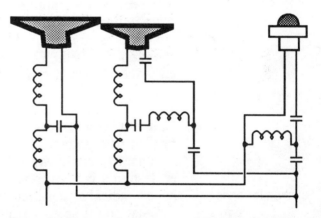

See what I mean? Now consider that some companies make four-way and even five-way speakers, and that, believe it or not, some speakers (not many) use fifth-order filters!

There are other problems with crossovers of course. Look at the drawing of the first-order filter earlier in this chapter, and notice that the coil is placed in series with the woofer. That coil is composed of many turns of magnet wire, which is not easily confused with audiophile-grade speaker cable. That coil has both inductance and DC resistance. It behaves not unlike a length of thin, cheap hookup wire. A few bright designers, by the way, use a minimum number of turns in the coil, and then increase inductance by using a ferrite or iron core. This works very well, except that at a certain current the core will become magnetically saturated, and the coil will then think it has much lower inductance.

extra parts

Real-life speakers, I might add, often include parts other than the ones shown in my illustrations. Extra capacitors or coils may be added to compensate for small problems in frequency response, nearly always at the cost of extra time distortion.

I would still rather do without a passive crossover, as I was saying earlier. I consider the cost of one or two extra power amplifiers to be money well spent. I am willing to agree, however, that it is possible to build a passive crossover which does not call undue attention to itself. The formula for building such crossovers does not, alas, seem to be known to everyone.

Can you "hear" a crossover?
by Gerard Rejskind

What's the best way to know whether your speaker system's crossover network is well designed? I have a radical idea. Listen to it.

listening for phase errors

What you'll hear — if it's there — is a phase error...woofers, tweeters and other drivers that are out of step with each other. This goes beyond mere crossover errors. Note that some loudspeakers use offset drivers — typically the tweeter will be further away from you than the woofer. You would be correct in surmising that the phase would be wrong if the drivers were just mounted into the front of a flat board.

That said, you can get rather quick at spotting phasing problems by listening to good speakers and comparing them to less good ones. Certainly you won't have much trouble finding "less good ones," because they're in the majority. Especially awful are so-called "rock" speakers, apparently named for their total inability to reproduce the sound of acoustic instruments. Also ghastly are those no-name speakers often included in the system-of-the-month at certain stores. Or just look for any small rectangular box with a huge woofer. The designer of that one will have made some lulus, and odds are that he did not have had a sudden flash of lucidity when he was designing the crossover.

what to listen for

What do you listen for? Paul Bergman points out in the preceding section that the most audible phase difference is heard when there is a time difference between the tone coming from the woofer and the same tone coming from the tweeter. Naturally those two tones will partly cancel, and so there will be a depression in frequency response at the crossover point. The frequency measurement method used by many manufacturers, which consists of placing a microphone right up to each driver individually, will not show up this problem. A listening test will, however, because the sharp slopes of the depression are accompanied by a resonance. That resonance will make it sound as though you were listening with a mailing tube up to your ear.

problems in the highs

In fact what you'll hear depends on the frequency of the crossover point. Phase shift between drivers is unavoidable at higher frequencies, because the wavelengths get so short that just moving your head slightly will change the apparent phase between drivers. That is why no loudspeaker can reproduce a cymbal so that it sounds real. At longer wavelengths, however, it's a different matter.

Those three-way and four-way speakers built by

junk peddlers usually have a crossover point right in the midrange somewhere, between 200 Hz and 1.5 kHz. Unless phase is correct, the error will be annoyingly audible on voices. Pick a voice, any voice. It can belong to Barbra Streisand or Luciano Pavarotti, or your local FM announcer. There may be a pinched, nasal quality to it, and perhaps even a hint of a lisp. There will be a certain prominence to sounds of the offending frequency...and this, please note, is despite the partial cancellation of the sound between the two drivers. The prominence is caused by the resonance associated with the response notch. If the phasing problem is relatively high in frequency, it will almost certainly affect sibilant sounds. Esses will have more of a "shhh" sound. That can be caused by a poor pickup, turntable or preamplifier, but if one speaker does it and another fed from the same source doesn't, it's a crossover problem.

using voice to spot problems

There is scarcely a crossover problem that cannot be diagnosed with voice, because voices are such a familiar sound. Close your eyes and imagine that it belongs to someone right in the room. Can't do it? There's something wrong. Resonances in the speaker enclosure? Possibly. Poor design of the crossover? very likely.

The two may well go together, of course. Audio design blunders are a bit like rats. You never have just one.

Alternative technologies: the search for the perfect speaker
by Paul Bergman

cone speakers

The good old cone speaker is now more than 60 years old. It is, along with the internal combustion engine and the tungsten light bulb, one of our longest-wearing pieces of technology. Take a woofer or midrange driver from any current loudspeaker, and place it alongside the speaker from a 1932 *Philco* radio...and you'll have to look hard to see the difference. The dynamic cone speaker has survived because it is simple to build, small, and easy to use. And with careful use it can give superb results.

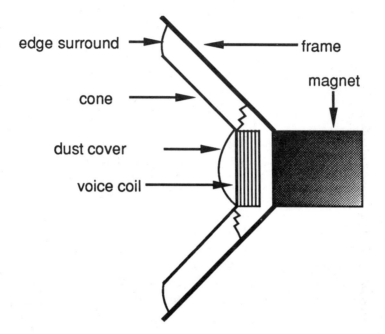

edge surround → frame

magnet

cone →

dust cover →

voice coil →

simplicity

Simple is the word for this speaker. A coil is hung in the magnetic field of a large permanent magnet. When the signal current flows through the coil, that coil becomes an electromagnet, whose polarity depends on which way the current is flowing at that instant. As it varies, the coil is either attracted or repelled by the permanent magnet, and it moves either backward or forward. A paper (or plastic) cone is connected to the coil. and it too moves back and forth.

Simplicity is its biggest advantage. Electromagnetic technology is so familiar and so well-developed that it's not much of a trick to build a reasonably acceptable driver. Indeed, it's easy to buy a driver off the shelf, and most driver manufacturers will build one to your specs.

The electromagnetic driver has disadvantages too, and they are numerous.

For one thing its relatively small diaphragm (the cone) is a poor match to the large air mass of the room. It's like trying to push a car using matchsticks. This considerable problem is responsible for the very poor efficiency of dynamic speakers: typically only four or five percent of the signal from the amplifier is turned into sound. The tiniest sealed enclosures actually take 99% of the power of your amplifier and heat the room with it. Only with special techniques, such as with horn enclosures, can this problem be even partly overcome. At the same time the cone of a speaker of any size has lots of mass, and therefore lots of inertia. It's tough to get it moving, and just as tough to stop it.

For another thing it cannot be used all by itself. It requires considerable cabinetry, which accounts for nearly all of the cost of most speaker systems. These cabinets, incidentally, introduce difficult technical problems of their own. They vibrate, they store energy for release at a later time, and they mostly don't do what the theory says they're supposed to do.

Finally, dynamic speakers suffer from electrical problems. Voice coils are (you guessed it) coils made up of long lengths of wire which has considerable resistance, which prevents the amplifier from controlling speaker motion properly. Coils also have inductance, which behaves like a filter for high frequencies...tough in the case of a tweeter!

Solutions? There are dozens, even hundreds. These are a few of them.

Feedback. As you may know nearly all amplifiers use "inverse feedback" to reduce distortion: part of the output signal is sent back to the input for comparison and correction. Wouldn't it be nice to include the loudspeaker in that feedback loop. But how?

You could put a microphone inside the speaker enclosure, as one manufacturer did a long time ago, and feed its output back to the amplifier. Other manufacturers included an extra voice coil on the woofer, which did in fact act like a microphone whose signal was sent back to the input of the amplifier. This was a little cumbersome, unfortunately, except in the case of one such unit, which had an amplifier integrated into the speaker itself.

One small French speaker uses a simplified form, where the output of the second coil goes to the crossover network rather than the amplifier. Finally, several European speakers use what could be called mechanical feedback. Two woofers are mounted so that they face each other. The motion of one tends to oppose the motion of the other. The intended purpose is the same as that of voltage or current feedback used in amplifiers.

maximum
efficiency

Horn loudspeakers. This is virtually the only design to tackle the problem of impedance mismatch between the speaker cone and the room. It uses an "acoustical transformer," a long tapered throat that tapers exponentially, with its small end next to the speaker and its large end in the room. Public address horns use the same principle to get lots of acoustical power from relatively small amps. They have lousy bass, however, because a horn must have a mouth width of one quarter the wavelength of the lowest frequency to be reproduced. Hi-fi horns such as the legendary *Klipschorn* are folded upon themselves for compactness. Even so a horn with a mouth width of one meter (that's a lot!) would not reproduce sound below 55 Hz. That's why hi-fi horns are placed in corners, so that the walls and floors can form an extension of the horn mouth. Fifty watts in a large horn is like 400 watts in a small sealed enclosure.

new materials

Polypropylene speakers. The cone of a loudspeaker should act like a piston, moving back and forth as a unit. The different parts shouldn't vibrate in relation to each other. Traditional speakers are made of paper, which is light and non-resonant but not terribly stiff. Speaker cones have also been made of aluminum (too resonant) and bakelite (too massive). Chemical "doping" with sticky substances have been used to improve the stiffness, and such plastics as Bextrene have been used too. A current favorite is polypropylene (usually, but not always, transparent), which can be made at once light and rigid. Speakers made of this material can be driven harder without problems.

These improved materials are often accompanied by a cooling system, using ferrofluid. This is a magnetic fluid which gets just as hot as metal does, but which "mates" better with the surrounding structure, and therefore conducts heat better.

new principles

Piezo tweeters. Certain synthetic crystals, when stressed, emit an electrical current. Such "piezoelectric crystals" are used in the very cheap phono pickups supplied with portable record players. The crystals can also be reversed: run current through one, and it will twist. That is how piezo tweeters work. They have very high impedance, so that they don't load down the amplifier, and they also don't have a coil to filter out the highs — or to burn out. There's only one problem, really. Piezo pickups sound horrible, and the piezo tweeters we've heard are of similar quality.

Ribbon speakers. This too is a reversed transducer. The ribbon microphone was popular in studio recording some years back, and is still used even today. A slim ribbon is stretched across an extremely powerful magnetic field. As it moves, an electric current is induced magnetically through it. The ribbon loudspeaker is a reversed microphone. Once again a narrow ribbon is stretched in the field of a large magnet. The audio signal passes through a transformer (so that it can match the impedance of the ribbon — a mere fraction of an ohm) and hence through the ribbon itself. Essentially this is a conventional electrodynamic speaker, except that the ribbon replaces the voice coil. Since the ribbon has almost no inductance (to store energy and delay the signal, to say nothing of filtering the high frequencies), the amplifier can exert very tight control over its motion. Nearly all ribbon speakers are tweeters. There are some very cheap ribbon tweeters (even *Radio Shack* has one) but good ones can cost well over a thousand dollars each. Incidentally, it is possible to build a large full-range ribbon speaker. The *Apogee* is a notable one.

radical technology

Ionic tweeters. There was only one of these ever, the *Ionovac,* later marketed only in Europe under its original name of *Ionofane.* This unusual tweeter had a pair of rods like the ones welders used, to produce electrical arcs to ionize the air. The loose ions were then manipulated electrically by the *Ionovac's* unusual circuit. The diaphragm was the air itself, so it had few problems of excessive inertia. Frequency response extended to radio frequencies. Unfortunately the ionic tweeter needed service every few hundred hours, and it couldn't handle more of a tenth of a watt of power, which rather disappointed the rock fans...and anyone else who wanted to listen above a whisper. As a "bonus" it produced ozone gas. We'd like a little more of this near the North and South Poles, but not in the living room, please. Ozone is toxic.

Electrostatic speakers. This is perhaps the most radical of speaker technologies, and it has popped up with regularity over more than three decades. Electrostatics have no magnets and no coils. Instead they have two fixed perforated metal plates, called stators, and — in between them — a light membrane called a diaphragm. A power supply places a few thousand volts DC between the two stators. No current flows, since they are a small but significant distance apart.

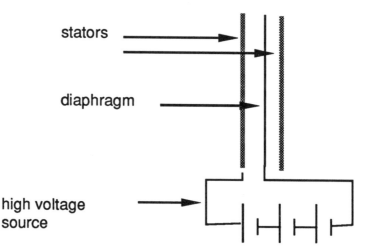

stators

diaphragm

high voltage source

how electrostatics work

The audio signal passes through a transformer so that it too is at a high voltage, and runs between the diaphragm (which is a sort of metallized Saran Wrap) and one of the stators. As the electrical charge on the diaphragm changes, it will be attracted either toward the front stator or the rear one. As it moves, it produces sound.

Many people who have never heard electrostatics find them — you should pardon the expression — electrifying. The diaphragm is so light it can react to the audio signal nearly instantaneously, giving a "snap" to the midrange that is astonishing. Plucked instruments, such as guitars and basses, come to life in realistic fashion. The best electrostatics must be heard to be believed.

So why aren't all speakers electrostatics?

Because this technology also a down side. Electrostatics are large and difficult to fit into most decors. That's especially true because they emit sound from both front and rear, which means they don't like being placed near walls. On the other hand they have power supplies that must be plugged in to the wall — an extra cord to trip over.

There's lots more nasty stuff. Electrostatics don't have great bass performance, unless you make them wall-sized — in which case you lose the advantage of the lightness of the diaphragm. The high frequencies are not that perfect either. The ideal speaker would be a "point source," with all sound coming from a single point in space. An electrostatic panel is the opposite of that — it is a large radiating surface. For the same reason, although these speakers may give an excellent left-to-right stereo image, they will "flatten out" recordings, obscuring the feeling of depth of good recordings.

fragility

As if that weren't enough, electrostatics are fragile. Overdriving one can cause an electrical arc — a miniature lightning bolt — between the diaphragm and one of the stators, and then it's game over; the resulting hole in the diaphragm will run like a 1946 nylon stocking. There are ways around this flaw. *Martin Logan* speakers use heavy Teflon insulation to prevent arcs. The *Quad* ESL-63 has a circuit that senses the ionization of the air that immediately precedes an arc; it will short itself out to save itself...possibly taking out the amplifier! And of course a lot of amplifiers are taken out by electrostatics anyway. To an amplifier they look like capacitors, which is not what amplifier designers anticipate when they do their stuff.

why bother?

So why bother with these finicky speakers at all? Well, there are some sounds they can reproduce better than any other device, and their excellence can be addictive. They can make conventional speakers

118

sound muffled and electronic. That makes it hard to go back to ordinary speakers.

having it all

And if you want it all (or *almost* all) there is the hybrid speaker: a large electrostatic panel covering most of the audible frequencies, plus a conventional woofer taking care of the extreme bass that the electrostatic isn't comfortable with. Marrying these two very dissimilar speakers is matchmaking of a high order, however, and it does not always result in wedded bliss.

Understanding speaker specifications
by Paul Bergman

It was some years ago, I recall, that *Studio Sound* magazine (published in the UK but distributed world-wide to the trade) printed a somewhat aggressive editorial defending its practice of not publishing any loudspeaker specifications in its surveys. It suggested that any studio owner who thought that speaker specifications, other than SPL ratings, meant anything must be out of his mind.

Though I might be a little less harsh than *Studio Sound* was, I must concur that there are problems with loudspeaker specifications, and indeed with loudspeaker measurements. I have been asked to write about this in the past, in the pages of *UHF,* but I note that many people still do not understand the nature of loudspeaker specifications, the way they are determined, and their meaning...if any.

power handling

Among the general public (a population sample presumably different from the readers of this magazine) the specification most mentioned is power handling, or — as it is misconceived — simply power. "How many watts is it?" will ask the prospective consumer in the store. Many people are genuinely hazy on this question, as though they thought a loudspeaker actually has power, as an amplifier does. "How many watts will it take?" would of course be a much better question, but even so there would be no clear answer.

Speaker manufacturers are reluctant to use figures that are completely straightforward. A straightforward power figure, in my view, would answer the following question: what is the maximum power that this loudspeaker will accept, at no more than a stated level of distortion, at any frequency from (say) 50 Hz to 15 kHz, for an indefinite period of time, without sustaining damage? Unfortunately a typical answer might well be 5 watts, and in many cases only a watt or two. In a few cases the answer would be best expressed in milliwatts! This would not be a great booster for sales, however, and such a speaker may in fact be assigned a rating of 100 watts. This figure is bound to be somewhat arbitrary, and it is interesting to look at how the manufacturer might come up with it.

The question is, what happens if you actually feed a 100 watt signal into that loudspeaker? If the signal is at 50 Hz it will probably result in unacceptably high harmonic distortion, possibly reaching as high as 90%. If it is at 10 kHz it will almost certainly cause tweeter failure within a second or two, and even if it is at 1 kHz, sustaining it might cause damage to the woofer within 20 seconds. Any iron-core coils in the crossover network will probably be saturated, causing gross errors in the frequency response, and potentially opening the way to damage of the drivers. Considering these rather depressing facts, how do we justify a rating of 100 watts?

Generally, manufacturers don't take distortion into account, but consider only the survival of the speaker. They also generally assume that their speakers will be used with music, not with test tones. It is rare for music to include very high-powered high frequencies, for instance, because acoustical instruments cannot produce them.

danger:
synthetizers

Synthetizers can, of course, and the emergence of synthetized rock music twenty years ago was accompanied by an epidemic of blown tweeters. Furthermore music has a certain "duty cycle." Even loud rock music provides full power signal to the speakers only 70% of the time, whereas with classical music it is more likely to be 30%. The speaker maker will therefore assume that his "100 watt" speaker will receive 100 watts at most 70% of the time, and that the tweeter will never receive more than 10 watts, and even so not continuously. These may be dangerous assumptions, but that is what lies behind that "100 watt" rating. I think it is best to ignore power ratings entirely, and to pay attention, instead, to the wording of the warranty, and to its exclusions.

suitable amplifier
size

Even more doubtful is the manufacturer's rating of the suitable size of amplifier to drive the speaker: say, 20 to 200 watts. The lower rating is presumably the minimum power that will produce satisfactory level with that speaker. However there are so many variables — room size, acoustics, listening habits — that this means little. Maximum amplifier power means even less. A perfect amplifier, which would not clip at any power level, and therefore would have an infinite power rating, would not be particularly prone to blowing speakers, though it could certainly be used to do so. On the other hand a small amplifier, if it is driven hard enough that it begins clipping the signal, can be used to burn out nearly any tweeter.

Now let us move on to other specifications.

I have already written about the difficulties of evaluating speaker frequency response. Very simply it is impossible to know which method is fairest. There are several possible methods:

The anechoic chamber, which absorbs all reverberation, so that you measure only the wave coming from the front of the speaker. However this does not correspond to the conditions of real use, and will make the speaker seem bass shy and overly bright.

The FFT test. FFT stands for "Fast Fourier Transform," a high-speed calculation done by computer. Since large anechoic chambers are so expensive, some companies use pulses which can be analyzed in a fraction of a second, before the first echo has time to return from the nearest wall or even from the floor. The FFT method certainly saves money, but presents the same problem as the anechoic method.

The standard room test. Frequency response is checked in an ordinary room, to give a reasonable assessment of how it will actually sound. Bass will seem more prominent, since the bass coming from the back of the speaker will be picked up by the test microphone, whereas off-axis treble probably will not. Of course the room's acoustical peculiarities, including its standing waves, will be reflected in this test. Note that the measurement done by *UHF* is a variation on this method, using a real room, though hardly a conventional one.

The multiple microphone method. Here, we go back to the anechoic chamber, or else we use the FFT test, but this time with several microphones placed around the speaker, so that rearward dispersion can be taken into consideration. I think it is misleading to suppose that a handful of readings can be used to represent what is really happening around the speaker. Furthermore some such tests do not consider phase. Out-of-phase signals, which in real life would cancel out, are shown as adding. Such a test is worse than useless.

The near-field test. To minimize the contribution of the room, microphones are placed very close to each of the drivers, perhaps within a centimeter. This yields very attractive figures, but is highly

a cheaper test

a still cheaper test

other tests

misleading. First, tiny differences in microphone placement cause large differences in readings. This is especially true if a cardioid microphone is used, in which case the result will be purely arbitrary. Secondly, placing the microphone so close does not take into consideration the impedance match of the driver to the room. For non-technical readers I might describe this as the speaker's ability to control the room's air mass. This impedance match is usually quite poor, but it is not absolutely consistent from one speaker to another. Finally, once again some manufacturers "forget" to correct for differences in phase among drivers. This is a major problem in certain speakers, but exists in even the best designs.

measuring efficiency

The one speaker specification that appears to have some relation to reality is the SPL rating. SPL stands for "sound pressure level," and the SPL rating is the output level, measured in dBa, at a distance of 1 meter on axis when the speaker is driven by 1 watt of power. This varies typically from 86 to 92 dBa. This isn't a very wide variation, so small errors make a large difference. Now if you've understood my explanation of the difficulties of measuring frequency response, you will see right away that measuring SPL is also problematic. Unless this is done in an anechoic chamber (very expensive and not accessible to many manufacturers) then room standing waves, coupled with very tiny differences in microphone placement, can easily make a difference of several dBa.

measuring impedance

Finally let us consider speaker impedance, which looks on the surface as though it should be completely straightforward to measure and to rate. It can certainly be measured easily, but rating impedance is every bit as arbitrary as rating power.

I know some readers may not be clear on just what impedance is. They know it is measured in ohms, and they realize that resistance is also measured in ohms. Real-life speakers are not pure resistances, however. They also have inductance and capacitance, which may be in series with the resistance, and/or across it. Inductors (which are coils) behave like resistors that increase in value as frequency goes up, whereas capacitors behave like resistors whose value decreases as frequency rises. The combined ohm value of this complex network is called impedance. Naturally impedance will vary with frequency.

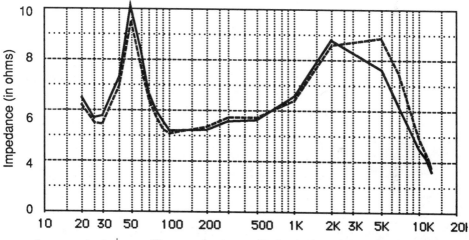

only a nominal figure

To see how much it varies, look at the graph of the impedance of a typical "8 ohm" speaker.

As you can see the impedance strays rather far from the nominal 8 ohm rating. What's more, the impedance curve is not quite the same at all power ratings. The solid line shows the rating with 0.5 watts of power, whereas the dashed line shows the rating with 5 watts of power (for reasons already mentioned it is not safe to run impedance tests at higher levels). This is by no means an extreme case: some loudspeakers dip down to 2Ω and up to 40Ω. We should not be surprised that amplifiers sometimes find the job of driving a loudspeaker difficult.

choosing
specifications

What else could one measure? To be sure there is the question of harmonic and intermodulation distortion, but most speakers have such high distortion that such ratings are unlikely to become popular with manufacturers. There is also the question of phase coherence, which can be measured with quick pulses, or (as *UHF* does it) with a square wave. Testing a number of speakers clearly indicates that designers tend to give priority either to optimum frequency response or to phase integrity. To some extent one has to choose.

choosing methods

To do this, of course, one also has to choose among several possible measurement methods. The choice is always difficult to justify, and any designer who does not spend a great deal of time listening to actual music through his prototypes is propelling his company in the direction of trouble.

Recording

Record companies wish you would leave the recording to them, and simply buy their products. But consumers have their own priorities, and many audiophiles want tape decks.

Young listeners, who buy most records, use tape decks as their major music source...which is the reason cassettes outsell CD's and LP's combined. Older audiophiles prefer the latter two media, and they make their own cassettes for their cars or their Walkmans. All groups (and this is the part record companies dread) also use tape decks as a primary source of music: they borrow records from friends, rent them from the library, or simply record from FM.

There are several ways to record music.

Open reel decks

remember open reel?

Once very popular among audiophiles, open reel decks are now nearly extinct, and indeed most hi-fi stores don't stock them. If you want one, you'll have to call one of the companies that cater to the professional and semi-professional users. Because the market for open reel recorders is now rather small, most companies have left the field. Essentially, then, you will have the choice of three brands: *Revox, Teac,* and *Otari.* It is interesting to note that even *Sony,* which did much to popularize home recording, no longer makes analog open reel recorders.

There is still a good reason to use open reel: quality. A good open reel machine is far superior to the finest cassette deck. Armed with a good noise reduction system, it can actually yield lower noise than even digital recording. These machines can also be used without noise reduction. A large proportion of "audiophile records" are made with relatively low-

126

cost machines, with no noise reduction.

more than frequency response

The advantage of open reel tape is less evident today than it was, because modern cassette decks have little problem maintaining full frequency response. Response isn't everything however. It is interesting to note that frequency response tests on cassette decks are done at a level 20 dB below maximum level. Why? Because otherwise the high frequencies would overload the tape.

Why should that be? In order to minimize noise, cassettes are recorded with greatly boosted highs, just as long playing records are. The highs are equalized (rebalanced so they are normal) during playback. But the highs are recorded at very high level, and they can overload the tiny tape.

less need to equalize

Similar equalization is done on open reel tape as well, but is less radical. Recorders operating at 19 cm/sec are commonly tested at 10 dB below full level, and professional machines operating at 38 cm/sec or more can withstand frequency testing at full level.

But that isn't the only advantage of open reel tape. These large machines are less vulnerable to certain problems that plague cassette tape.

other open reel advantages

One is *modulation noise*. This noise can be readily heard if you record a pure tone: on playback an unpleasant crackling sound will accompany the tone. Modulation noise is caused by a slight unevenness in the thickness of the tape's magnetic coating. It doesn't show up in conventional noise figures, since it can be heard *only* when other sounds are being recorded. Modulation noise on a good open reel machine is far lower than it can be on a cassette.

Another is *scrape flutter*. This is different from the conventional flutter caused by errors in machining of the recorder's parts. Magnetic recorders, like turntables, are sensitive to vibrations. Vibrations that travel down the length of the tape cause the tape to move slightly forward and back, causing a variation in speed. Scrape flutter is so called because it is often caused by the scraping of the tape against tape guides and other non-moving parts. The best recorders include large rollers to trap vibrations, but there is no room for such rollers inside the tiny cassette. Scrape flutter is too rapid to be perceived as a speed variation, and it casts a veil over the music, rather like intermodulation distortion.

too expensive

However there are economic reasons that militate against the domestic use of open reel tape. For one thing the tape itself is priced astronomically at the retail level. A one-hour tape can easily cost over $50! It is far cheaper wholesale, but you have to establish an account with the supplier, and you need to buy in large quantities. The tapes are bulky, too, and of course they fit neither your car nor your Walkman.

Cassette decks

This is by far the preferred way of taping at home, and for good reason. Inexpensive decks are readily available, and the tapes are especially cheap. This is especially advantageous if you want to copy records. And the tapes can be listened to anywhere: at home, in the car, or on the bus.

For most purposes a moderately-priced tape deck is fine, since very high quality is wasted on the majority of car stereo systems and portable players. If you're looking for maximum quality, however, there are some features to look for.

good features to
have

Three heads. The best decks have separate circuits for recording and for playback. For one thing it means that each is optimized for the job it must do. And it also means that you can listen to the tape as you make it. As the tape moves past the three heads, it is first erased, then recorded, and finally played back. What you hear, then is the *actual* sound of the

128

cassette, a fraction of a second after the recording is made. This feature is expensive however.

mechanical quality

Two capstans. The capstan and pinch roller are what move the tape forward and determine its speed. They are normally placed after the tape heads, but some machines have a second capstan and pinch roller before the heads. The tape against the heads is then in a "closed loop" which is isolated from the cassette mechanism. Speed will more accurate, and overall performance will be far superior.

Variable bias. Ultrasonic bias is a very high-pitched tone which must be mixed with the sound during recording, to avoid excessive distortion. Add too much and you get high distortion and low recording level. Add too much and the bias (which is identical to the current that powers the erase head) will begin erasing the highs as soon as they are recorded. There is an optimum bias level for each tape, and some recorders have a front panel knob for setting it. This is especially useful with three-head decks, since you can make instantaneous comparisons of the original signal and the tape, and adjust the bias until the two sound alike.

self-alignment

Automatic alignment. There are two aspects to alignment besides bias. One is *equalization,* the amount of treble boost during recording. The other is *output level:* it must be right if the Dolby noise reduction circuit is to operate correctly. With most decks, adjusting those means a trip to a service shop. But a few decks have computer-operated alignment circuits. You put in a tape, push the alignment button, and wait a few seconds. Naturally automatic alignment requires three heads.

We do not recommend buying an auto-reverse deck, unless it will be used for background music. Designing a cassette deck is difficult enough; designing it to work well in either direction is virtually impossible.

what cassettes to buy

Blank cassettes are very low in cost, as we've noted, and that's especially true if you buy them from the grubby little specialized stores that abound in larger cities. The cheapest tapes are "Type I," and use a magnetic coating of conventional ferric oxide. For nearly all applications the best Type I tapes are adequate. However you would be well advised to stick with major brands, and to check the country of origin as well. For instance, *Maxell* cassettes may be made in Japan (superb), Korea (quite good) and Mexico (unacceptable). Similar variations are common with all brands. Type II cassettes used to be made from chromium dioxide (as some *BASF* cassettes still are), but most now use some other formulation which is, however, equivalent. Some Type II cassettes are superior to the cheaper ones, but in most cases the difference is inaudible. Type IV cassettes (there is no Type III) use pure metal particles. They cost a good deal more, but they are the tapes of choice for critical work. But beware: metal tapes require very high bias and erase currents, and even some machines with "metal" settings cannot furnish them.

Digital audio tape

is DAT for real?

These machines, popular in professional recording studios, were not yet commonly available when this book went to print. The DAT works like a miniature video recorder, which means that the tape heads are not fixed as in a conventional deck, but are placed on a rapidly-turning drum. The recording technology is identical to that of the Compact Disc: the DAT records data *about* the music rather than the music itself. The quality can be expected to be similar, then. In fact initially DAT sounds better than CD, probably because the code can be read with fewer errors. The tape wears rapidly, however, and there have been numerous reports of cassettes failing after a mere fifty passes through the machine! We don't know whether these problems are caused by problems in the formulation of the tape.

As we write this, domestic DAT decks will have an anti-copying feature. When a CD is copied, the deck will memorize its serial number. The machine will refuse to copy the same CD more than twice. Since the main use of DAT is to copy CD's, we predict that DAT will fail commercially.

Optical discs

As we write this, the recordable CD is a reality, at least in Japan. The present version cannot be erased, though erasable discs have been announced by several companies, and are being worked on...slowly. We believe this technology will eventually become commonplace, but the technical problems to be solved are enormous. What is more, no home recording system can become widespread as long as the recording materials remain expensive. Keep your eye on this, but don't hold your breath while you're waiting.

Video decks

This is the most widely ignored way of recording audio at home, and it's too bad. High fidelity video-cassette decks have nearly everything audiophiles look for. The best ones are hi-fi, sounding better than DAT, CD, cassettes or even open reel tape. The cassettes are very low in cost. And so are the decks.

Unfortunately they are getting a little *too* cheap. One feature which has been dropped from many VHS Hi-Fi machines is the manual level control. There should be both volume controls and level meters, not just an automatic level control.

The other rules of hi-fi shopping apply. VCR's, like all other electronic audio components, contain preamplifiers and other circuitry. In low-cost units, those circuits will be of mediocre quality. In more expensive ones, they *may* be superior. Unfortunately the few audiophile companies that manufactured high-end VCR's lost money at it. The cut-throat price competition makes profits impossible unless you slash costs to the bone...and the quality too.

A tip: VCR's often sound "wrong" at very low level. But they don't have to. Use good quality cassettes, and run them at maximum speed. Listen to a quiet passage, and adjust the tracking control (usually hidden under a panel) for best sound. This is doubly important for tapes that were made on a different machine. Note that the tracking setting for best picture will probably be slightly different.

Noise reduction
by Paul Bergman

The introduction of digital tape recording to the professional recording domain some years ago was done for a very particular purpose, which was to reduce noise. The noise improvement was earned at very high cost, the nature of which I have written about in these pages before. There are more conventional means of reducing noise, however, and for the home recordist they are for the moment of greater interest. They will remain so unless and until Digital Audio Tape becomes popular.

It is amusing to note that tape was once considered to be a noise-free medium, and that for this reason it was expected to replace the vinyl disc as the favored home recording system. Note that I am not speaking of cassettes — which had not been invented in the 1950's — but of open-reel stereo tape. Several manufacturers then sold such tapes for $25 to $30 (the equivalent LP then cost about $5). Such tapes were prestige items, since recorders capable of playing them back were as rare as they were expensive. In the years preceding the introduction of the

making good VHS Hi-Fi recordings

why digital tape?

45/45 stereo disc in 1958, they were the only route to home stereo.

However, the advantage everyone mentioned most often was noise. The tape was noise-free, hence superior. Listening to these tapes today is a curious experience, because in fact what you notice first is the objectionable level of hiss!

tape is noisier than we thought

Indeed it became quickly apparent that tape was a noisy medium, noisier in fact than the LP itself, as evidenced by the fact that, between selections of an album, you could hear the tape hiss vanish and reappear. The LP suffered from noise bursts, of course, in the forms of ticks and pops, but its average noise level was lower than that of contemporary professional tapes.

making quieter tapes

For that reason a great effort was made to make tape quieter. Tapes were run faster, at a dizzying 76 cm/sec (at that speed a large metal reel lasts only 16 minutes). Indeed some recordings were made on movie film recorders, onto 35 mm oxide-coated stock. These methods yielded only a small direct noise improvement. However using such high tape speeds and wide stock reduced the danger of saturating the tape with high frequencies. For that reason it was possible to record louder, to keep the signal above the omnipresent noise. Most tape manufacturers of the day offered "quieter" formulations, whose catalog numbers almost always began with "LN"…for "low noise."

It is educational to return to these old recordings, which often trumpet their technological daring ("Recorded on 35 mm film!") in bold lettering. Listening to them is nearly always a disappointment, however. By modern standards these are hissy recordings, and the soft passages are often unlistenable.

Manufacturers launched crash programs to reduce noise. The *3M* company built an ingenious tape machine which used two channels per stereo side, one of which recorded at 20 dB greater level than the other. The loud one distorted on the peaks, whereas the soft one was noisy on quiet passages, but a control circuit monitored levels, and switched to the better of the two tracks, with levels adjusted to sound the same. This machine yielded an impressive 20 dB reduction in tape hiss, but its non-standard configuration doomed it. At the same time, some other companies began looking at a noise-reduction device which had been around since the 1930's: the compander.

the first noise-reduction system

"Compander" stands for "compressor-expander," and the actions of these two devices are shown in the illustration on page 135. These units were often used on long broadcast lines, which — like tape — suffered from excessive noise. The compressor processed the sound at the input end, squeezing the loud and soft sounds closer together, thus keeping all of the sound well above the noise. At the other end an expander "unsqueezed" the sound again. As the soft passages were pushed down in level, so was the accompanying noise. If companders could work on broadcast lines, could they not work as well with tape recorders?

But the concept was difficult to sell to recording studios, because recording engineers often had enough broadcast experience to be aware of the disadvantages of companders. The major disadvantage is that, despite the apparent symmetry of the diagrams shown in this article, the process is not symmetrical at all. There is no way for the expander to know what the original level was, because that information is simply not preserved. For that reason the slope of the resulting graph (input level versus output level) is not the 45° line it should be. A second problem is that the variations in the noise floor as the music level changes is quite audible. There is noise during music passages, but it drops away during silences. This effect is known as noise modulation. Finally, the compression and expansion slopes, since they are applied by different machines in different locations, may not be perfectly matched. You can hear the devices "pumping" the noise. This is known as "compander pumping," especially audible on voices and on percussion, and it long plagued broadcast networks in the days before quiet satellite channels.

noise reduction that failed

Considerable work was done on companders. Units with carefully matched compression-expansion ratios were built. The most promising innovation was a compressor which provided an extra signal, corresponding to the amount of compression it had done at any given moment. This information would be recorded on an extra tape track, and could be fed to the playback expander. The expander would now have the information it had been missing, and it could reconstitute the original level perfectly. No one wanted to "waste" tape tracks however (studios seldom had more than three-track machines), and the whole effort died when a new innovation appeared on the scene.

enter Ray Dolby

It was Dolby noise reduction.

What Dolby did was so radical that few recording engineers initially believed it could possibly work. The audible frequency range was split with filters into five different bands, and companding was applied to each. The five were then mixed back together at the output. Dolby offered two advantages over the old compander. Noise modulation could not be heard, because you would never get, for instance, a string bass modulating the hiss — the two were safely separated because of their differing frequencies. Also, the companding ratio was kept gentler, to minimize dynamic errors, and it affected only low-level signals, not loud ones. Finally, levels were carefully

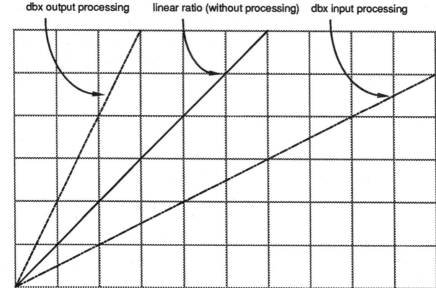

dbx output processing   linear ratio (without processing)   dbx input processing

Output level

Input level

set up using a series of "Dolby tones" which were recorded at the start of each tape, so that the playback unit could be adjusted for best results.

Dolby offered a 10 dB improvement in noise, and with the new advances in professional tape which had meanwhile appeared, it was enough to make hiss virtually inaudible. Dolby processors began appearing in studios worldwide, and the system soon became the de facto standard. Many of these units (today called Dolby A to distinguish them from later Dolby units) are still in use.

alternatives to Dolby

Not everyone fell into step with Dolby however. Some recording engineers were unimpressed with the 10 dB improvement in noise, and continued to favor a broadband compander. The best-known of these, and the most popular after Dolby, is dbx, whose principle is shown in the graph on this page. The dbx unit is a classic compander, with the advantages and disadvantages of such units. It cannot reconstitute dynamic levels perfectly, and the brutal compression/expansion ratio exaggerates problems in the tape recorder. On the other hand, because the ratio is linear, it does not depend on matching of input and output levels for correct operation. It also offers 30 dB of noise reduction instead of 10 dB — which means that a dbx tape is *100 times quieter* than a Dolby tape!

the noisy cassette

None of this was terribly helpful to the audiophile, however. As records became quieter, home tape seemed all the noisier by comparison. As for the newest tape medium, the Philips Compact Cassette, it was simply too noisy for anything but casual listening. Ray Dolby turned his attention to home recording, and designed what he called Dolby B.

reducing cassette noise

Dolby B was a simplified version of the expensive Dolby A used by studios. There was no splitting of the sound into different bands. Rather, the Dolby B circuit was a variable high-end boosting filter. On soft passages the highs were boosted by as much as 10 dB to help them override tape hiss. Loud passages were not processed at all, since they don't really need noise reduction. On playback, the highs are reduced by 10 dB during soft passages...and the hiss is reduced at the same time. From a much simpler system came the same 10 dB reduction afforded by the expensive Dolby A.

Indeed the B system was in some ways better. Because it processed only the highs, there were fewer errors in dynamic level, less chance of audible pumping. Many people wondered why Dolby B could not be used in the studio as well. In fact it cannot. The very slow cassette tape achieves its wide frequency response through the use of large amounts of high-frequency boosting, which produces a great deal of noise at the upper end of the audible range. Reducing upper band noise is enough to yield a 10 dB improvement. Professional tape runs as much as 16 times faster however, and its noise is much more evenly distributed across the frequency range. For that reason it takes a broadband system like Dolby A to improve it significantly.

the Dolby problem

Unfortunately Dolby B continues to suffer from its Achilles heel: the need for accurate level matching. Unless the playback unit receives the correct level from the recorder, it will not know how loud the original signal was, and it will not know how much to roll off the highs. Most home users wouldn't put up with aligning their recorders to a standard "Dolby tone" at the front of each tape, and so Dolby B circuits are aligned to a standard "Dolby level" (often indicated on the recording meters with the "double-D" symbol). Most machines cannot be aligned for correct Dolby level by the user. In any case, if Dolby level adjustment is correct for one brand of cassette tape, it will be wrong for a tape which has a higher or lower output. Thus Dolby recorders often have poor frequency response with the Dolby circuit switched in.

newer Dolby

Most modern machines now offer an alternative system, Dolby C. It uses a second processor, which acts further down in the frequency band, well into the midrange in fact, yielding a 20 dB overall improvement.

The disadvantages of Dolby account for the continued liveliness of the dbx system. Like Dolby B, home dbx differs from the professional version, but the principle is exactly the same: a 2:1 compressor is used to make the recording, and a 1:2 expander is used for playback. The improvement is still 30 dB. The effect can sometimes be heard, and the process exaggerates flaws: a 3 dB dip in frequency response becomes a 6 dB dip, and a 6 dB "dropout" (caused by a flaw on the tape) becomes a 12 dB dropout. On the other hand dbx operation does not depend on level matching. The dbx system is especially popular for multi-track cassette units used by musicians to make demo tapes. Since tracks may be mixed and re-recorded several times, they need all the help they can get.

But now allow me to return to the question of professional recording. Some readers will be aware that some "audiophile" recordings are made without noise reduction of any kind, and yet do not suffer from excessive hiss. That reflects the considerable improvement in recorders in the past decade and more. The first professional recorders (the *Ampex* 350 for instance) had a signal/noise ratio (the difference between the loudest recorded sound and the tape noise) of only 50 dB. By 1970 that figure had risen to 60 dB, and it now stands close to 70 dB. Indeed with the best analog recorders (which place two stereo tracks on double width tape) the S/N ratio can easily be 73 dB. This is more than a two-hundredfold improvement, and it is good enough to be subjectively silent at any reasonable playback level (though of course it will grow worse if the tape is copied). An improvement of 10 dB to 30 dB can be achieved with the addition of Dolby A, Dolby SR (the newest system), or dbx noise reduction. This will actually outperform digital tape.

This might conceivably be overkill. A number of "purist" record producers refuse to use noise reduction, because no circuit which uses so many filters and chips can possibly sound transparent. At one time their records would have been characterized by hiss. Today they are not. This is true even if the producer has chosen, as some do, to capture the full dynamic range of the music, with neither compression nor manual adjustment of levels.

Home recordists are not in the same fortunate situation however, and it is difficult to enjoy cassettes without noise reduction. For commercially-made cassettes Dolby B is the medium of choice, because it is most widespread. For cassettes you make yourself, Dolby C is far superior. I expect that Dolby S, the new domestic version of Dolby SR, will be better yet, but of course Dolby S tapes will not play well on older machines.

what to use for cassettes

Speaking for myself I would not make cassettes with dbx unless I were making a musical demo tape and were needing to record and re-record a great deal. The deterioration of the already dodgy cassette medium is just too gross. Also, unlike Dolby cassettes, dbx-processed material is unlistenable on car radios or portable players that don't have dbx decoders.

Of course, deciding might turn out to be easier than it looks. Most modern cassette recorders offer both Dolby B and C, and some have Dolby S. A few offer dbx as well. The latter machines are ideal of course: you can try every system made with your own music, and adopt the one that sounds best to you.

Off the air

Tuners don't have a good reputation among audiophiles, and it's easy to see why. For the most part FM radio sounds dreadful, and most tuners are built to suit the medium. Still, a good tuner is an invaluable part of any music lover's system. Even if you have a large record collection, you can hear only a fraction of the world's music. Your key to the rest is the radio. Fidelity is secondary. First you need to *find* the music. Later, you can buy the recordings, if they appeal to you.

do you need a good tuner?

Before you decide on a tuner, you should know that most FM broadcasts don't justify a quality tuner. Ready for a horror story? Here is how and why broadcasters *deliberately* make FM into a low fidelity medium.

Inside FM
by Gerard Rejskind

Most people suppose that FM radio stations have the very finest of high fidelity equipment. And on the surface that assumption makes sense. Isn't FM referred to as "hi-fi radio?" Aren't "professional quality" and "broadcast standard" the most impressive boasts to be found in audio advertising? And besides, radio stations can afford the best, can't they?

is "hi-fi radio" for real?

In actual fact, of course, a quick tune across the FM band will reveal that the term "hi-fi radio" has become a little hollow. The most noticeable characteristics of FM stations are narrow, ragged frequency response, lack of plausible stereo effect, and extremely high distortion. The larger the city, the more that will be true. One culprit is ignorance. The other is necessity. And sometimes it is a little hard to tell one from the other.

broadcast turntables

Take broadcast turntables...please!

It seems fairly obvious that a *Linn* Sondek wouldn't survive until the next commercial in a typical FM station, and neither would most of the serious competition. All turntables with spring suspensions are out, because you can't afford to let the turntable move and make the stylus skip a groove. The typical radio station turntable is mounted solidly into a massive steel cabinet, sometimes on stiff rubber bushings that serve largely a cosmetic purpose. Belt-driven turntables are out too; a Canadian company, *McCurdy,* introduced one more than two decades ago. It accelerated like a Lada with a tankful of Gatorade, and the company eventually gave all its clients their money back.

So what *do* they use? That depends. A surprising number are still using idler-driven, or puck-driven turntables...so-called because a miniature hockey puck transmits the power from the motor shaft to the platter. The *QRK* is one such turntable, and some stations still have vintage *Rek-O-Kuts* (an apt name, since "wrecking cuts" is exactly what these products are good for). More modern stations have direct-drive turntables, nearly always the *Technics* SP-10 Mk.II. This is far from being a bad turntable, and its acceleration and reliability make it by far the best choice for radio station use, but unfortunately its virtues will be lost in the gear that accompanies it.

tone arms and pickups

The arm notably. I can't see our *Alphason* tone arm making it in a modern station any more than the *Linn* would. Disc jockeys want huge arm lifts they can handle with mitts, and they don't have time for sissy stuff like cueing devices and anti-skating pulleys. Nor will they baby thousand dollar bearings. So stations use arms with extremely high mass that have very tight bearings. Though the SP-10 turntable is expensive, the typical arm mounted on it typically costs less than $150 — and we're not talking discount prices here. The *Micro-Trak* arm, no longer sold but still found in many stations, was made of wood. It was a 1950's design, intended to work with the very massive and stiff phono pickups of that day. Unfortunately its replacement is little better. It is fairly typical of what you'll find on a complete $120 Japanese turntable.

And what kind of phono cartridge do you suppose they mount in these museum pieces? Don't expect to find a *Koetsu* or a *Talisman,* because you won't for several reasons. First there's the mass of the arm. A massive arm will tend to have a low resonance, and for that reason it won't play the station's prodigious collection of warped records. It won't...unless the great stiffness of the pickup's stylus assembly drives the resonance back up again. So very stiff pickups are used, nearly always cheap ones (the *Shure* M-44 is still found in many stations, as are ruggedized *Stanton* and *Ortofon* cartridges). Moving-coil pickups would be out anyway, because the life expectancy of a stylus in a studio is not exceptionally high, not when the DJ has five seconds to cue a new hit while a choir is singing the praises of Nick's A–1 Used Cars. Stations buy stylii by the gross, and don't want to squander their profits on beryllium cantilevers and *van den Hul* line-contact diamonds.

studio furniture

We've already established that most broadcast turntables are suspensionless, but in fact there's worse. The large steel bases used in some large studios are too big for smaller stations. So both turntables will be mounted, typically, in the same plywood tabletop, with nothing to insulate them but a sheet of Arborite. So vulnerable are they to vibration that, on some stations, if you listen with big speakers you can hear turntable two being cued while turntable one is playing!

There is no reason not to use the best associated electronics, and in fact some stations do quite well

144

here. *Bryston* sells, in good quantities, a special studio version of its .5B preamplifier. Here and there you'll see a high-end home preamp, like an *Audio Research* or even a *Krell*. In all too many stations, however, the preamps are cheap and dirty sonic horrors, with performance no better than you could have gotten in 1954. They are durable and noise-free, which reassures the station engineer, but the list of their virtues ends there.

studio loudspeakers

Let us pass over the monitor amplifiers and speakers used to judge this dubious sound. Sometimes they are quite good (*Bryston* again, plus such speakers as *JBL, Energy* and *Tannoy),* and sometimes they are sonic horrors. The source is so poor, however, that there is no possible way even the best monitor can make it sound good. Disc jockeys tend to listen very loud, because the source material is sonically so confused that only at high level can individual instruments, and even vocalists, be made out.

microphones

Turntables are not the only station sources, however. There are three others, the best of which is live studio. Thousand dollar condenser microphones are typically used, nearly always mono unless there are two voices. The other two sources are not so good.

other sources

One, obviously, is Compact Disc. FM has done a lot to promote the CD, because even a mediocre CD player is audibly superior to what passes for a turntable in the same studio. That's one reason radio converted to CD early (the other reason is that CD promoters gave the stations not only the discs but the players too). Many a station is still using those first-generation CD players, which sound harsh and metallic. Of course even they sound wonderful alongside broadcast cartridges. These are endless tape loops, working not unlike the late, unlamented 8-track home cartridge. Frequency response is very poor, distortion is high, and hiss is prominent. Also, because the tape is continually being pulled from the centre hub, and therefore stretched a bit, the speed is shaky and so is the phase relationship between channels. I know of a station that some years ago began playing all of its music from cartridge. The phase error between the channels was so high that the top two and a half octaves cancelled out if you listened in mono! Changes were quickly made.

making a bad signal worse

But frankly the quality of the source is not FM's only problem. A funny thing happens to it on its way to the transmitter...except that there really isn't anything funny about it at all. It's called *signal processing*.

There's one signal processor that stations have little choice about using: the limiter. North American FM stations are limited to a frequency deviation of no more than ±75 kHz. The Ministry of Communications hires inspectors who make spot checks of the on-air signal, using a deviation monitor (which is not as perverted as it sounds!) to verify modulation. Anyone going over the maximum gets a citation. The limiter prevents the signal from overmodulating the transmitter. Any station that didn't plan to get one wouldn't receive its broadcasting licence in the first place.

How much it harms the fidelity of the station depends on how hard the limiter is driven. If the signal never reaches the limiter's threshold point, then the limiter does not actually do anything, and of course its effect will be inaudible. If, on the other hand, the signal constantly comes up against the threshold, the limiter will begin to act as though it were a different instrument: a compressor.

making the station louder

A compressor does exactly what you'd expect, as you'll see from the graph on the next page. It does to the signal's dynamics what a steamroller does to asphalt. The soft passages are made louder, sometimes nearly as loud as the peaks. This destroys the structure of the music — assuming it has a structure

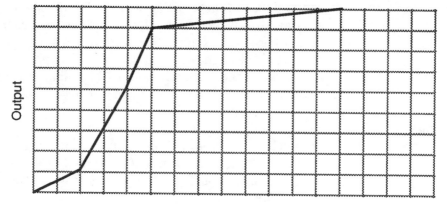

Output

Input

a better
compressor

to start with — but it achieves the station's goal, which is to have the loudest signal in town (surveys show the loudest signal draws the most listeners). But of course when a major city has 23 radio stations, all with compressors on line, don't expect much in the way of musical subtleties, because you'll be courting disappointment.

Not all compressors are the same, by the way. Modern ones are called gated compressors. The electronic "gate" keeps careful track of the signal level. It will bring up the level on soft passages, unless they are too soft, in which case it won't. This prevents it from increasing the level on background noise making it as loud as the loudest music. Unfortunately some stations are still using ungated compressors — or are overdriving their limiters, which comes to the same thing. When you come to the end of a song which simply fades (quite common, since many songwriters don't know how to compose endings), you don't actually hear the fade…just the noise that gradually comes up to meet the music.

There is more…and if you are squeamish you may want to stop right here.

There is a particular variety of compressor that does far more than the ordinary sort. It divides up the signal into five distinct frequency bands. Each band is then separately compressed. What comes out of this unit is then recombined and sent on to the transmitter, or — as is more likely — to the next signal processor. That processor is quite likely to be a de-esser, a device which applies compression only to the upper midrange, to lower the level of a vocalist's sibilant "ess" sound. It has side effects as you can guess. Some stations "widen" their stereo image by using a device which adds a slight delay to one of the two channels...thereby destroying, in fact, all stereo information.

making the sound worse just for fun

Last but hardly least, there is the audio exciter. This device, originally made by *Aphex,* "enriches" the sound by adding extra harmonics. That happens to correspond to our definition of harmonic distortion, but some stations pay good money to do exactly that.

I could go on, since obviously some of the transmitter audio circuitry itself is less than sonically transparent, but I'm sure you get the idea. In many a station, there is a war between the chief engineer, who may actually be an audiophile, and the manager, who is more often a pecuniaphile — a lover of money (look it up, Latin scholars). Of course perhaps some money can be made by a station that sounds better than the others, instead of just louder, but not many stations are grabbing for that brass ring.

Which is not to say that all stations suffer from all the worst problems. I expect to get lots of mail from station engineers who run their shops differently. Well, good! By all means write, and I'll be happy to hear from you.

And if you have a moment, whisper a little message into the ears of your colleagues, okay? Tell

148

them that not everyone listens to FM on ghetto blasters.

Choosing a tuner

Are you ready to buy a quality FM tuner anyway? Perhaps we can help in your choice.

Tuners, like amplifiers, come with a number of published specifications. Among them are sensitivity, selectivity, capture ratio and distortion.

Sensitivity is usually specified as the minimum signal needed to obtain a given amount of *quieting*. If you have 40 dB of quieting, then the noise will be 40dB lower than the maximum level of the signal. That isn't a very good noise figure, and you will want at least 60 dB of quieting before you are likely to consider the reception acceptable. But if you read the specs carefully you may notice that sensitivity is frequently specified for *monophonic* signals. You will need far more signal to listen in stereo...which is what you will probably want to do.

Selectivity is the ability of a tuner to receive one station without interference from other stations. Adjacent-channel selectivity refers to interference from the station next door: stations at 97.9 or 98.3 MHz if you are tuned in to a station at 98.1. Alternate channel selectivity refers to interference from stations two positions away: in our example, 97.7 or 98.5 MHz. Most tuners are quite good at this, but this specification is misleading. What limits the selectivity of most tuners is *images*. A strong station will overload the tuner's front end, and there will be distorted replicas of its signal appearing at one or more places on the band. If a distant station you want to hear is on the same frequency as an image...too bad.

Capture ratio refers to the ability of a tuner to discriminate among signals on the same frequency. If your tuner has a capture ratio of 3 dB, then if you

tuner specifications

keeping out unwanted stations

want to hear station A while ignoring station B, station A must come in 3 dB louder (twice as loud) as station B. The best tuners actually have capture ratios of 1 dB or less. That figure is especially important to avoid *multipath distortion.* That's the FM equivalent of TV ghosts, and it's what you get when you receive not only the main signal from the transmitter, but also one more (slightly delayed) echoes from nearby buildings or mountains. Multipath can make an FM signal unintelligible, but a small amount of it can add harshness to an otherwise good signal.

the tricky question of distortion

Distortion usually refers to *harmonic* distortion, the generation of non-musical harmonics by the tuner. Most tuners have very low distortion...in mono. Not all manufacturers dare to specify stereo distortion, which is typically much worse.

tuning accurately

In any case, a tuner will yield its best performance when it is tuned *precisely* on a station. This is harder to achieve than you might think. Many tuners have "AFC" (automatic frequency control) circuits, to pull the tuner onto the right frequency. Those seldom work quite right. Try this: tune carefully to the very centre of a very clean station, using only its manual tuning aid. Then turn on the AFC. You may actually hear the distortion *increase* as the AFC pulls the tuner off frequency. That's not all. Most modern tuners have given up conventional tuning methods in favor of a system known as *frequency synthesis*. A sophisticated low-cost chip allows the tuner to invent the appropriate frequency tone, so the tuner can synchronize to it. There is nearly always a small difference between the synthetized frequency and the station signal, however, and the result is *much* higher harmonic distortion than specified. The very best tuners (which, alas, are quite costly) still use analog circuitry. That sometimes means they won't have presets for instantly finding your favorite stations. However some have built-in frequency counters, which allow you to see the frequency you're tuned to on a numerical display, just like the ones on synthetized tuners.

a good antenna

High performance is costly, and it's important to know that some (though not all) of a tuner's weaknesses can be compensated for by a good antenna. A directional antenna with a rotor can pull in a strong signal even from a distant station without also pulling in multipath and interfering stations. If you already have a TV antenna on a rotor, you may be able to run your tuner from it, unless it has a filter in it to cut out the FM band. An antenna costs a lot less than an ultra-sensitive tuner.

instead of an antenna

Does your landlord threaten you with a lawyer when you mention putting up an FM antenna? The alternative to an antenna is a signal amplifier, which fits between the antenna and the tuner. Unfortunately most inexpensive signal amplifiers (around $40) cause more problems than they solve, because interfering stations also come in louder, and they are more likely to overload the tuner and cause images. A better device is a *tuned* signal amplifier, which amplifies only the frequency it is tuned to. The only one we know of, the Canadian-built *Magnum Dynalab* Signal Sleuth, works very well. But of course you need to tune both it *and* the tuner when you change stations. Too bad if your tuner comes with a remote control.

How good a tuner do you need? If you listen to live concerts, then get one of the same quality as the rest of your system. If you listen only to record shows, buy something cheap. It will still be good enough to let you discover a new world of music.

What about AM?

It's well known that AM radio stations are losing audience, supposedly because of their sonic inferiority compared to FM. That's ironic, considering the extent to which broadcasters deliberately sabotage FM sound. But, as you might suspect, they do the same thing to AM. And AM tuners are built to suit.

the state of AM tuners

In fact they're even worse than the signals, which is saying something. Most manufacturers just don't care about AM. Signal-to-noise ratio is typically only 30 dB, harmonic distortion is nearly 10%, and frequency response extends from 200 Hz to 2 kHz, less than the bandwidth of the telephone! You're lucky if you can understand the news!

It doesn't have to be that way. It is *possible* to build an AM transmission and reception system with a 50 dB signal-to-noise ratio, 1% distortion, and frequency response from 20 Hz to 15 kHz. A few (*very* few) stations still pride themselves on such standards, but to know which ones, you'd need a tuner of similar quality. Good luck!

high fidelity AM?

A few high fidelity AM tuners have been marketed over the years, but they haven't had commercial success. In order to get a hint of how could AM could be, you'd need to buy an old tuner, one with wide bandwidth. It would probably be over a quarter of a century old. And it would probably use tubes.

Sorry. AM *could* be high fidelity, or close to it. In most cases, unfortunately, it makes the telephone seem like high-end audio. We should be raising hell with everyone responsible!

" IT'S JUST AS WELL THAT THE EQUIPMENT NEVER ARRIVED. WE'VE GOT TWELVE CONFIRMED ORDERS, ALREADY! "

How to buy

hi-fi and mid-fi

Why is it so difficult to find a needle in a hay-stack? Because at first glance those bits of hay all look like needles. Why is it so difficult to find a true high fidelity store? Because at first glance a lot of other stores look like hi-fi stores.

Most "hi-fi" stores are not high fidelity stores. They do not sell high fidelity equipment, and they cannot demonstrate high fidelity to you. In our circle they are referred to as "mid-fi," a term which may seem like moderate praise. However "low-fi" is usually reserved for the worst of the ghetto blasters and the thirty dollar Walkmans.

It is mid-fi stores that are mainly responsible for the poor reputation of high fidelity in the general population. They *say* they are selling hi-fi, and indeed the products they stock bear some of the world's most respected brand names: *Sony, Pioneer, Technics, Mitsubishi,* etc. Many people are seduced by the shiny panels, the beautiful knobs, the digital displays, the shimmering grilles, the boom of the bass, the tizz of the treble. And they buy. But others are repelled, liking neither the looks nor the sound. "If this is hi-fi," they figure, "you can keep it. I just want to hear a little music."

Those who buy often come to agree. The gadgets quickly pale, as gadgets do. And the loud boomy music, for all its initial impressiveness, grates on the nerves. Once the thrill of the new purchase is gone, the listening sessions become shorter and shorter. Ultimately the system is turned off forever. The owners stops buying records (why buy what you don't listen to?), and won't buy any more equipment either. "I don't want to spend the money," he or she will say. "I really don't listen to records all that much."

154

"Why not? Don't you like music?"

"Yes, of course I do. I *love* music."

"It's curious, then. Haven't you wondered *why* you've stopped listening to it?"

listening for music, not noise

In fact, of course, what the mid-fi buyer has *actually* stopped listening to is not the music, but the unpleasant noise the mid-fi system produces. Music is composed of a number of diverse elements: melody, rhythm and harmony. A poor system can reproduce none of these accurately. Not many consumers have the self-confidence to affirm that an expensive famous-name piece of electronics cannot even begin to serve the purpose for which it was allegedly created. So they blame themselves. "I don't have enough of an ear," they will say.

The truth is, of course, that they have all too *good* an ear!

everyone can hear the difference

And before we go on let us build up your self-confidence a bit. In our listening tests, we frequently work with neophytes, people who have never heard hi-fi before. We do it because we want to check whether outsiders can hear what we hear, so we don't talk each other into imagining things that aren't there. Amazingly enough, *they always can!* People introduced to hi-fi for the first time can hear differences among very expensive preamplifiers, for instance...differences the mainstream magazines claim are imaginary, by the way. They have definite preferences, and more often than not, their preferences agree with ours. So much for weight of experience! You *can* hear what's good, providing you listen to the right thing (the music, not the sound), and providing you don't get overawed by the sales clerk or by the famous name on the front panel.

But of course you cannot judge hi-fi unless you can hear it, and in most stores you cannot hear it. How do you find a store where you can? Before we attempt to answer those questions, let us first cover the history of the modern hi-fi movement. In that story is the answer to what you want to know.

how high-end hi-fi began

The schism between genuine hi-fi (sometimes called high-end audio) and mid-fi is relatively recent, dating back less than twenty years. It was created by the forces of inflation, which drove up the costs of building audio equipment just when the general public was starting to get a taste for it. There was a pronounced shift in the audio market. The Japanese, with their superior production techniques, were better able to keep prices down than were American companies, which related on crude, labor-intensive assembly techniques. Many American manufacturers either folded, or went off to build something more profitable, like weapons. The major Japanese trade marks became household words.

inflation

But something else happened too. As inflation gathered force, ultimately breaking the 10% line, good quality equipment got harder to sell. Consumers who were used to the idea that they could get a "nice little music system" for $600 *still* wanted to pay $600. The big companies gave them what they wanted, because the customer is always right. Wood cabinets turned into veneered chipboard, and then into *vinyl* chipboard. Discrete transistors gave way to cheap integrated circuits. Big transformers were replaced by tiny transformers. Japan's crack engineers found ways to slash production costs and still deliver the same excellent audio specifications.

a new movement

But there was growing dissension. The specifications were good, there was no doubt about that, but the equipment didn't *sound* right. What came out might be "hi-fi," but it wasn't music. And a few audiophiles — Canadians initially — got suspicious. They listened to British equipment, whose specs and creature comforts were no match for those of Far East products, *and they sounded better*. Why did a

156

British amp with 0.2% distortion sound better (more "musical," some said) than a Japanese receiver with 0.005% distortion? There must be more to hi-fi than specs, surely. Perhaps other phenomena, previously unknown, accounted for the difference. The mainstream magazines poured scorn on such "fantasy," as they still do. So did most audio salesmen.

the movement spreads

But listening was believing, and as more and more people listened to this esoteric gear, the belief spread. Small manufacturers in Canada, the US and elsewhere abandoned the search for ever better paper specifications, and began actually listening to what they built. A few salespeople, who had heard the difference for themselves, quit their jobs and opened their own stores, dedicated to the demonstration of *genuine* high fidelity, to equipment that could reproduce music enjoyably.

better stores

Such stores had to be superior to ordinary stores, of course, because they could succeed only if consumers could be convinced that hi-fi was to be judged with music. That meant setting up proper listening rooms, with proper acoustics. It meant getting rid of "comparator boxes," which allow instantaneous A-B comparisons, because those boxes added distortion to the music.

higher prices

And it meant selling at comparatively high prices, for several reasons. For one thing the new manufacturers could not take the music-destroying shortcuts that were now endemic in Japan. For another the equipment was addressed to a minority, and it was not possible to save money through large-scale mass production. For yet another, if the store was going to set up a proper listening room, hire knowledgeable personnel, and take the time to demonstrate equipment thoroughly, it had to be paid for its trouble. And so high-end hi-fi equipment was expensive, as it still is. "High end" refers to price as much as quality.

(The price need not be completely out of sight, however, so relax! Read on.)

mid-fi evolves

In the meantime the mainstream stores (the mid-fi stores) evolved too. They could no longer sell equipment on the basis that it sounded better (since they could not demonstrate its superiority), and so they competed on price. Heavy discounts became common. Service was reduced, since there was no longer enough profit to pay for more than a cash register. Consumers were hustled through the showroom quickly, their credit cards were click-clacked through the machines, and they were sent back to their cars with instructions to pick up their stuff "at door C on the west side of the building." Other products shared the floor space, to help pay for soaring rents: TV sets, VCR's, microwave ovens, and cellular phones.

telling good stores
from bad

Now at this point we need barely tell you how to tell one store from the other. You need a store that has a genuine listening room that is closed off, with acoustical treatment. You need a store with chairs that are comfortable to sit in. You need a store without comparator boxes, in which there aren't three dozen pairs of speakers huddled together (the ideal number is one pair). You need a store which — like us — puts a good deal of importance on the quality of the source used for demonstrations. You need a store where you will not be rushed. You need a store that makes you wish you could stay and listen longer.

(*An important aside:* some stores are hybrids, and have characteristics of both. That is true of some very large city stores, which have both hi-fi and mid-fi sections. Just don't buy from the wrong section. It is also true of some small town stores, which can't survive on hi-fi alone, and therefore must sell everything from TV's to toasters. A very small store can, in some cases, even give you better service. But insist on the listening room, the absence of a comparator box, and the time to listen. If the store doesn't have that, do your shopping on your next trip to a larger centre.)

How do you find the right stores?

finding a good store

We'd suggest picking them initially by what they sell. The yellow pages are a good place to start. There's nothing wrong with a store selling *Yamaha* or *Sony,* but an ad built around such brands probably indicates a mid-fi store. When you're searching it's helpful to be familiar with some genuine hi-fi brands. Drop around and have a look. Closed listening rooms? Chairs? No comparator box? No mounds of loudspeakers? So far so good.

how much to spend

It is conventional wisdom that you should decide on how much you want to spend before you set foot in the store, and then stick with it. But that makes no sense. How, for instance, would you decide that you want to spend $2000? *Why* that amount? How do you know that's enough? In fact (let us dream a little), how do you know it's not *too much?* Seasoned audiophiles may be equipped to make this sort of advance decision, but someone starting out can't. Could you decide how much you wanted to spend on a car if you had never *seen* a car?

This gets awkward because there's every chance the sales clerk will actually ask you how much you want to spend. A good answer is that you want a system that will reproduce music enjoyably, and that you are there to find out whether this store has such a system, and, if so, how much it will cost. It is then the clerk's move, and if he knows what's good for him, he will reply with a convincing demonstration, not with empty words. By all means sit down and listen.

bringing your own record

Ideally, in fact, you should listen to a recording you brought along, either LP or CD. Good stores encourage you to bring your records. If you don't, a competent sales clerk will ask you what sort of music you like, and even invite you to look through the store's collection. There is a special advantage to bringing your own however: if this demo doesn't work out, you can go listen the same recording in another store.

good store, bad demo

This would be a good time to mention that even the best stores don't always do good demonstrations. Everybody has off days, and you may have come at a bad time. That's all right, you probably won't want to buy the first time out anyway. What you *will* want to do at the end of the demonstration is discuss with the sales clerk (a) what you liked, (b) what you didn't like, (c) what you should probably listen to next time, and (d) when a convenient "next time" would be.

choosing in the right order

Remember to select the components in the natural order, from upstream to downstream: source (turntable or CD player), preamplifier, amplifier, and speakers. Bad stores will try to sell you speakers first.

Don't be overawed by anything — not by what the sales clerk says, not by the name on the equipment, not by the price tag, not even by what we tell you. You haven't come to do what this book says, but *to check out whether what is in this book is right*. Your own judgement is the definitive one.

However we will encourage you to listen in an appropriate way, which is to say, in a fashion we find helpful for ourselves.

A-B tests

For one thing, don't try to switch quickly from one component to another. The mainstream magazines love this sort of "A-B test," because (they claim) auditory memory is short, and only with quick changes can you compare two components. That's silly. If auditory memory were so short, you could buy the worst piece of trash in the store, and you would be perfectly happy with it, because by the time you got it home you would no longer remember what better systems sounded like.

Beware of A-B tests! They are pseudo-science. Some time ago we did our own interesting little comparison: we synchronized an audiophile recording on our reference turntable with a *copy* of that record on cassette. When we switched back and forth rapidly, even experienced listeners could not tell us which was which. Indeed, in most cases they could not reliably tell *when* the change was made. However anyone who listened to each all the way through was in little doubt as to which of the two was the more satisfying.

looking for
satisfaction

What you are seeking is *long term listening satisfaction*. If a system is obviously offensive, there is little point in continuing, but if something seems acceptable, then listen for a while. It may seem to get worse, or it may remain good. Give it time. After a half hour, do you feel like listening some more? When you return for a second visit, do you want to hear the same system, or are you eager to push on? Be in tune with your feelings, and trust them.

different
components,
different stores

Comparisons can become nearly impossible if two components you are considering are sold by different dealers, and therefore can be heard only in different rooms, with different systems. The only solution we know of is to take extra time, and to test the component's capacity for making you feel right about music. The individual details (bass, treble, smoothness, image, etc.) may be impossible to compare, but satisfaction isn't. Some dealers, if they sense that you are serious and may actually buy, may even arrange a test in your own home.

That, of course, points up the importance of having a good relationship with your dealer. Once you have a store that you know won't steer you wrong, it's worth doing your buying there, even if it means choosing a brand that dealer sells rather than what a

magazine recommends.
Even ours.

One more thing...

Allow us to add what our friends who own audio stores would like us to say. If you've read this chapter all the way through, you now know that there are two kinds of stores: high-volume stores with small profit margins, and full-service specialty stores which, of necessity, need higher margins to fund the facilities and service they offer. *Don't get the two confused!* Specialty stores may have sales on discontinued models, and they may offer specials once a year, but generally they sell at full list price. If you want to haggle, do them a favor, and go to a mid-fi store instead. But remember: the best bargain is not the system with the lowest price; it is the system that does exactly what you want, so you don't have to replace it a year later.

Think it over.

"YOU WERE RIGHT.
ACOUSTIC TILES MAKE A BIG DIFFERENCE!"

Installing it

Installing It

Choosing your new hi-fi system may have been difficult, but your problems are not yet over. Now you have to install it. As we shall see, installing a sound system is more like installing a bathroom than like plugging in a toaster, and it may require the aid of as many professionals.

Or it may not, depending on how handy you are with your hands. But this is no place to take short-cuts. You may have gathered from the previous chapters that manufacturers go to great lengths to get their components "just so." You don't want to lose the benefit when you are this close to your goal.

In this chapter we will cover several topics: where to put the equipment, how to wire it up, how to place the speakers, and — last but not least — what to do about the acoustics of your listening room. Once again, you may find that what we tell you runs exactly counter to what you may have read elsewhere.

Where to put it

"rack" systems

If you have visited some of the mass-market warehouses we warned you against in the last chapter, you'll no doubt have noticed that many one-brand systems sold in those stores come with their own "racks," which are in fact narrow sets of shelves with glass doors. Those racks are usually of thin chipboard with only enough structural strength not to collapse under the weight of the equipment...or at least not right away. However racks are a key aspect of the warehouse's marketing effort. You'll get a super "deal" on the equipment itself, and then the salesman will ask innocently whether you would like to have the rack too. (Silly you...you thought it was included; well it isn't, and the markup on it will be very high). Of course we don't recommend you get that sort of rack, if only because we don't recommend you get that sort of system, and we don't recommend you go into that sort of store in the first place. Unless you need a VCR.

don't buy one

But aside from the aspect of value (high price and poor construction), there are other reasons not to get that sort of cabinet. Audio components run hot, and indeed some of our favorite components run *very* hot. That heat needs to get out into the environment, otherwise it will build up in the equipment, shortening its life, and perhaps even causing sudden failure. Most racks are small, with closed backs and glass doors that most people keep closed even when the equipment is on. This is about as good a recipe for disaster as one could devise.

other cabinets

Which is why some companies build *open* cabinets. The best known of these companies is *Target,* though several competitors have equipment tables that look strikingly similar. The frame is welded steel, and the shelves are wood. On some models, the top shelf is different from the others. It is made of a material called *Torlyte,* a light, labyrinth-like structure that resists transmission of vibrations. The *Torlyte* panel rests on four spikes which further decouple it mechanically from the rest of the stand. The feet of the stand have spikes of their own. You may have guessed that the top shelf is meant for a turntable, but in fact the turntable is not the only part of the system that needs mechanical decoupling.

amplifiers and vibration

It has been known for some years that even electronic components, such as amplifiers, are sensitive to vibration. Turn an amp all the way up (with no signal going in, of course) and slap it with your palm. Do you hear a noise from the speaker? With many amplifiers you do. The best designers now pay attention to what is known as the *microphonic* aspects of an amplifier, which is to say that they go to some trouble to make the more sensitive circuits and components shock-resistant, so that they don't act like microphones. But of course it is clearly not a good idea to subject even the best amplifier to external vibrations. That's why good stands have spikes on the bottom.

Many people are worried about those spikes, by the way, because they fear they will ruin their carpets and floors. That isn't necessarily true. If you have carpets, the pointed spikes will go between the loops of fiber and through the backing, doing far less damage than the blunt foot or caster of a conventional cabinet, which will crush the loops. The spikes *will* make holes in a hardwood floor however. If you have a fancy floor and no carpet, you can place something under each of the spikes, such as a penny.

vibration and CD players

Naturally CD players are at least as sensitive to vibration as an amplifier or a preamplifier. For one thing a player *contains* a preamplifier. And for reasons we've already explained, the disc mechanism has a difficult enough time getting code off the disc when all is running smoothly. What it doesn't need is vibration from the speakers or anything else shaking it up so it loses track of what it is supposed to be doing. Some CD players are more sensitive to vibrations than others, but all are best placed somewhere stable and insulated from whatever else may be going on.

vibration and turntables

But of course most sensitive is the turntable, since it is actually a vibration-measuring device. The turntable doesn't "know" whether the vibration it is receiving comes from the first violin of the Toronto Symphony or from the sneakers of your oldest child heading for a mid-afternoon snack. It sends on to the amplifier everything it detects. Interfering vibrations may or may not be clearly audible, but remember that even quite small vibrations can swamp the equally tiny vibrations which are the soul of the music. That isn't all. As we established in a previous chapter, the superior suspension of a good turntable allows it to reproduce low frequencies much more accurately, with a pleasing richness, but without annoying, artificial boominess. But the piece of furniture it is sitting on is *part* of that suspension. The phono pickup neither knows nor cares whether a resonance is entering via a poorly-tuned turntable suspension or through the thin panels of an audio rack. Even an economy turntable deserves a proper support, but if you've spent big money on a turntable, you can scarcely afford to ignore what it sits on. *The difference is not subtle.*

springy floors

Sometimes merely using a good stand with spikes is not enough. Some homes have poorly-suspended floorboards that are like trampolines. Despite the spikes, the vibrations from the speakers will travel easily through the boards and into the stand on which the turntable sits. What will be most noticeable is that walking by the system will cause the pickup to skip grooves. This is not an easy problem to treat. Footfalls on a typical wood floor produce vibrations of extremely low frequency, typically between 1 Hz and 4 Hz. No suspension system we know of is effective at such frequencies.

solutions

There can be other solutions, fortunately. Observe how the floorboards run (if your floor does have long boards rather than "parquet" squares), and get a look underneath the floor, if that is possible. Avoid placing the speakers and the equipment table so that they are at opposite ends of longitudinal boards. If there is a large and solid beam somewhere underneath the floor, it may help to place the speakers on one side of the beam and the equipment table on the other side.

This won't help with footfalls, of course, but we have a favorite way of checking out floor vibrations.

Place a bowl of water on the floor, walk by, and watch the ripples in the water. Move the bowl somewhere else, let the water stabilize, and then walk by again. Can you find a position where no ripples form?

Our magazine's reference system is placed in a room with the worst possible set of problems, by the way, so this is a topic with which we have considerable experience. The floorboards are wide and run down the length of the room. They are poorly supported, and, because they have been in place more than 140 years, they are bowed and springy. It is an understatement to say that we had problems with vibration, and we tried some rather draconian solutions. At one point, our turntable was on a layer of cork, sitting on a slab of marble, sitting on a very heavy solid steel table, sitting on styrofoam slabs, sitting on glass supports, sitting on heavy concrete flagstones. As you can see we don't fool around! Using a repeatable system for measuring vibration (dropping a weight at a precise spot and measuring the output from the cartridge sitting on an immobilized disc) we determined that none of these measures made *any measurable difference at all!*

We did solve the problem, however, with another *Target* product, the TT1 wall stand. We bolted it to a brick chimney, and now Jumbo the elephant could dance Swan Lake in our room without the turntable being any the wiser. This could be a useful solution for you too, but that is true *only* if you have a solid wall which is not merely resting on the floorboards, as many walls do. A wall stand works best attached to a load-bearing wall, one which actually holds up the house. It also works best if you can actually sink screws into wood studs, not just anchors into gypsum board. Note also that the stand must be *absolutely* level, which in older houses means it will *look* crooked because everything else is. Use an accurate spirit level, and take your time.

Speaker stands

If you have been reading this chapter attentively, you will already have guessed that, if the equipment should be decoupled from the floor, so should the loudspeakers. The more they move the floor structure, the more they will move your turntable, CD player and amplifier. For this and other reasons, "bookshelf" speakers are best not placed on bookshelves.

why you need
speaker stands

Some speakers, of course, are best not placed on anything at all, since they are clearly made to sit on the floor. In fact, however, they may not sound best that way. Even some large speakers can benefit from being raised a little, and sometimes tilted back a bit. There is a rationale for this. Most speakers do not yield accurate frequency and phase response over a wide angle. It would be nice if they did, but designers usually test their speakers "on axis," which means straight ahead, and so they don't bother much with performance off axis, which will be a mess. For that reason, it is best if the tweeter (or, better yet, the mid-point between the woofer and the tweeter) is on line with your ear when you are sitting down. Raising the speaker will accomplish this, and so will tilting it up a little. Some large speakers will perform better if placed on a low stand designed for it.

using spikes

What's more, the speaker should be decoupled from the floor with spikes, just as turntables and other equipment should be. The spikes can be mounted on the stand, or separate spikes can be added. Some audiophiles buy pointed aluminum feet with such brand names as *Tiptoes* and *Tenderfeet,* which are placed point down under the speaker. Decoupling the speaker in this fashion can prevent the excessively heavy bass that plagues many systems.

If you have smaller speakers, of course, you will

need stands for them. Some speakers have custom-built stands that are the right height (and are sometimes slightly tilted as well), but others merely come with a specification for the height of stand that should be used. The actual height you need may depend on the chair you listen from. The worse the speaker, the more sensitive it will be to height variations.

keeping the speaker still
The stand isn't there merely to place the speaker at the right height, by the way. A good stand will also keep the speaker from moving about. Newton would have understood this perfectly, since he predicted it in his First Law: *for every action there is an equal and opposite reaction.* As the woofer cone moves forward against the air, it tries to push the rest of the speaker system backwards. Since the cone has so much less mass, it will do most of the moving, but ideally it should do *all* of the moving. This means the speaker must be rigidly attached to the stand, and the stand must be attached rigidly to the floor...with spikes of course. Anything loose will move. This is important, because the mass of a speaker and stand can absorb a lot of energy...energy that *should* go into sound, but doesn't.

fastening the stand to the speaker
One advantage of custom-built speaker stands is that they often have holes which match threaded holes in the speakers, so you can bolt them securely together. All-purpose stands also have holes, but of course the speakers have no matching holes. Do you use wood screws, and risk damaging the speaker (whose crossover board may be sitting on the cabinet floor...)? If you're reluctant to do that, you can give the system some rigidity by using *Blue-Tak*. This Plasticine-like material comes under different names (*Fun-Tak* is another) and in different colors (it isn't always blue). It is available in stationery and hardware stores, and it is mainly sold for putting up signs and other objects without marking the walls.

We use it to fasten speakers we test to our stands. Of course our stands have spikes as well.

good stands

You're bound to notice that some stands cost more than others. The best stands are exceptionally rigid, and they are resistant to vibration. That means they must be heavy, and weight always costs money. A number of stands, including the ones we use, are made of heavy steel, and can be filled with sand to prevent ringing. If no sand is included, note that you need to use *kiln dried* sand. Ordinary sand contains moisture which will eventually rust the stands from the inside.

imitation stands

We might add that there is good money to be made by selling stands, and that several companies have noticed that it takes rather less technological sophistication to build a stand than it does to build a preamplifier or a CD player. The result is that there is a proliferation of stands from small companies that have ripped off the designs of the major companies. The ethics of such ripoffs may or may not bother you, but the standards of manufacture probably will. It is not easy to do spot welds so they don't show through the paint. For that matter it is not easy to get paint onto the steel so that it stays on. Good listening rooms tend to be rather dark, so be sure to look at a stand in bright light before you accept it. If it doesn't look good, buy your stands elsewhere.

Placing the speakers

There are few subjects in hi-fi more misunderstood than speaker placement. Even the "experts" often get this wrong. It's easy to confirm this by touring the booths at a hi-fi show. Exhibitors complain bitterly about the "poor acoustics" of hotel rooms, but they place their speakers with no regard whatever for the elementary laws of acoustics.

The first thing you (and they) need to know is that what you hear is not the speaker, but the speaker *and* the room together. That is especially true at lower frequencies, and it is this difference which makes speaker placement so important.

Higher frequencies tend to be beamed straight ahead, like the beam from a lamp. This is rather unfortunate, and it accounts in part for the rather poor performance of most speakers anywhere but straight ahead, but it is a fact of life. Needless to say, the surrounding walls don't affect the highs much. As frequency drops, however, the behavior of the sound waves changes. They become more and more omnidirectional, which means that they flow out like water from a burst container rather than light from a lamp. Deep bass is radiated in every direction. What happens to the bass that goes in other directions? Well, that depends on the room.

When you're trying to shout as loudly as possible, you probably place your hands around your mouth, like a megaphone. That does two things. First it beams forward sounds that otherwise would go to the side. Second — and unfortunately there is no non-technical way of expressing this — it improves the *impedance match* between your mouth and the atmosphere. Horn speakers, such as the famous *Klipschorn,* and public address horns use the same phenomenon to improve the transfer of energy from the speaker to the atmosphere.

If you place a speaker on the floor in a corner, it is easy to see that the floor and the two walls will form a horn and also have this effect, resulting in a better transfer of energy from the speaker to the room. At first glance this sounds like a good thing, but in fact it can be highly undesirable. Remember that it is *the lower frequencies* that are omnidirectional. For that reason the improvement in efficiency will be greater in the bass. Although you may be attracted by the idea of getting extra bass from a small speaker, you should know that it will not be

highs and lows are different

if you put the speaker in the corner

accurate bass. Most speakers are not designed to have normal frequency response in a corner, and the result will be a heavy and unnatural "boom-boom" sound that will muddy the music. The alteration in frequency response will be accompanied by an unavoidable ringing: the tendency of the speaker and room together to go on producing sound after the signal to the speaker has ended. That will further muddy the sound. Unless the speaker has been *designed* to go in a corner, you should avoid corner placement.

To a lesser extent, you will also get an exaggeration of bass by placing the speaker near any room boundary: two walls, floor and wall, or wall and ceiling.

staying away from walls

In fact we even avoid placing speakers close to walls at all. At the very least the omnidirectional bass radiating from the enclosure will shake up the structure of the house. Naturally we also don't like supports that fasten to the wall, unless the wall is made of concrete. Sometimes they're unavoidable, however.

avoiding symmetry

For some reason many homeowners are attracted by symmetrical decor, and they like to place speakers symmetrically, along a wall, with each speaker the same distance from the side walls. That will not give you the best sound (nor the best decor, in our view, though that is of course a matter of taste). Most rooms are prone to resonances that muddy the sound, and the best way to set up strong resonances is to keep all dimensions the same. That's the reason the worst possible listening room would be shaped like a cube. If you *must* use a wall, it's better to position the speakers asymmetrically. In our own listening room we place speakers at an angle to the walls, and that gives us by far the best result. We do the same thing when we attend shows in hotel rooms, needless to say.

There is another criterion in choosing a speaker position: stereo imaging. Most people place their speakers so poorly that they don't actually hear stereo at all. We recommend that, initially, you keep your speakers on long cables, even if those cables are of less than optimum quality. That will let you move them about freely. Too often, speakers are placed excessively far apart, so that there will be more "separation" between them. But it's not *separation* you want, it's the interaction you get when they work together.

testing stereo image

If your amplifier has a mono switch, use it; if not, listen to a mono source, such as AM radio or a pre-stereo recording. What you *should* hear is sound coming from an "invisible speaker" seemingly positioned between the real speakers. If you can hear *any* sound emerging from the actual speakers, then those speakers are placed wrong. Move them and try again. You may find that it takes a lot of moving about before it finally happens: the sound collapses into the centre.

Now return to stereo. The stereo field should expand out, and there should be a deep 3-D image. If at first you don't succeed, don't give up. Even poor equipment can be used to create a proper stereo image. Good equipment is, of course, better still.

Wiring it

At one time no one worried much about wires. Interconnection cables (the ones with coaxial phono jacks, which go between amplifiers and such things as preamps, CD players, tape decks and tuners) mostly came free with equipment, and most dealers would give you speaker wire when you bought a system. Typically it was transparent 22 gauge zip cord, which was easy to hide between the rug and the floor.

But over the past few years there has been a

174

growing awareness of the importance of good cables. Some modern cables cost as much as complete systems! The connectors are hand machined and gold plated. The wires themselves are made of long-crystal oxygen-free copper, or sometimes even of monocrystal silver! Some speaker wires are the size of garden hoses. The mainstream magazines continue to believe that the theories behind these fancy cables are mere witchcraft, but on the other hand none of them do their own equipment testing with 22 gauge zipcord anymore.

are the theories right?

Some of the theories undoubtedly *are* witchcraft. Some theorists claim certain cables cause phase errors because they transmit certain frequencies faster than other frequencies. Others claim that loudspeaker cables, like interconnects, must be shielded against interfering signals. As far as we are aware, such claims cannot be checked out scientifically.

But is hard to be too dogmatic about this, because there really *are* audible differences among cables. Good interconnect cables sound much better than the freebies that come with the equipment. And good speaker cables sound far better than ordinary zip cord, including the extremely big zip cords that can be purchased through industrial sources.

cables are hard to test

Unfortunately a cable cannot be tested quite the way an amplifier or a speaker can be tested. There is a great deal of interaction between cables and the equipment they are connected to. A cable that sounds good in our reference system may sound less good in your system, and vice versa.

when worse is better

Indeed, you may hear an improvement even if you use a worse cable. For instance, some amplifiers have frequency response that extends to several megaHertz, on the erroneous theory that wide bandwidth is best. Such amplifiers may run into trouble. Very high frequency signals (especially those from the best analog discs and from magnetic tapes) may be faster than the amplifier can handle. The result is an unpleasant phenomenon called *slew rate distortion,* or *transient intermodulation distortion.* If you feed such an amplifier from a poor interconnect cable, whose parallel capacitance actually short circuits some of the high frequencies, there will no longer be enough highs to make trouble for the amp, and it will sound better. Also, some poorly-designed amplifiers have unstable circuits which "ring" electrically. Using a speaker cable with lots of series inductance will limit the ringing, making the amplifier sound better...or at least less bad. But such mix and match "accidents" are not always serendipitous. Some early "audiophile" speaker cables actually had high *parallel* inductance. Some poorly-designed amplifiers, which rang electrically under the best conditions, actually went into runaway oscillation with such cables and self-destructed!

connectors | Hardest to test are connectors. A new connector, freshly fastened, will probably work well, assuming it fits at all. With time, however, common air pollution will cause tarnishing of the metal surface and a poor connection. Worse, the nature of the impurities from the air may be such that the connection will actually conduct electricity better in one direction that in the other. It then acts like the crystal in a crystal radio. Not only will it cause pronounced distortion, but it may actually bring in radio stations. The best connectors are plated with gold, which does not tarnish, and they provide plenty of pressure against the mating jack. (The junk makers, most of them in Taiwan, seem to have caught on to this however). Some expensive connectors from Germany, those from *WBT,* actually have locking collets which can be tightened to give a strong grip. However the benefits from such connectors may take months to show up, and they don't lend themselves to quick tests in the store...nor by a magazine.

trying cables
yourself

And so we will have to tell you that you will have to check out wires for yourself, with the set of components you have selected. Take your time. If you hear a difference, it isn't necessarily an improvement. Don't talk yourself into hearing an imaginary improvement simply because a cable is expensive and you figure it *has* to be good. It may not be. Or at least it may not be good *in your system.*

Room acoustics

It's obvious that the acoustics of your room must play a major role in what you hear, and that, in a real sense, the room is the final component of your hi-fi system. Yet magazines seldom touch the subject, and when exceptionally they do, it is to mislead. A number of magazine writers believe that, in order to get proper low-frequency response, it is necessary to have very rigid walls, preferably concrete, which will not flex, and therefore will allow the building up of maximum low frequency pressure. They are wrong. If they truly listen to music in such rooms, it is not surprising that they think all amplifiers sound alike.

acoustical basics

Telling you how to turn your listening room into audio heaven would take an entire book, and possibly one thicker than this one, so don't expect more than general principles. Still, armed with those principles, you should be able to plan your room a little more rationally, and improve the sound you hear more than a little.

A warning before we begin: *don't confuse acoustical treatment with soundproofing!* We will mention soundproofing — how to keep sound from getting out of the room — a little later on. For the moment we are talking about the sound that *remains* in the room. The two are completely, *utterly* separate.

Acoustics is something you can earn a degree in, and this chapter will not give you the knowledge of

---

a graduate acoustician. However the basic science behind the elementary principles of acoustics is surprisingly understandable. It all begins with the First Law of Thermodynamics, which most of us learned in high school:

Energy cannot be created or destroyed.

what happens to
reflected sound

What does this mean for our well-meaning magazine editor, doing his best to listen to music in his airtight concrete bunker? Well, we know that the speakers are releasing energy into the room in the form of sound waves. When a wave strikes a wall, a small percentage of it will be transmitted to the other side, where it will bother the neighbors, but not very much of it. Hardly any of it will be absorbed. Most will be reflected and return into the room. Indeed, it will be reflected a *lot* of times, as it goes back and forth. If it loses ten percent of its energy with each bounce (a not unreasonable assumption) then after 21 bounces it will still have more than 10 percent of its original energy (to calculate it, take 0.9^{21}, which is equal to 0.109), which means it will have dropped in level by less than 10 dB! It will take 65 bounces for the level to drop by 30 dB, and some 128 bounces to drop to 60 dB below the level of the original sound.

the long bounce

Those 128 bounces will take several seconds, even if the room is a small one. The time they take is what acousticians call the T_{60} time: the time needed before the reverberation decays to 60 dB (one million times) below the original level.

In our poor magazine editor's concrete room, all frequencies will have about the same T_{60} time, since concrete isn't very fussy about frequency. As we shall see, however, most materials *do* discriminate, and for the most part they absorb highs much more easily than lows.

Keep in mind that word *absorb*. And let us consider the opposite of the concrete bunker, namely the anechoic chamber. Such chambers are maintained by a few (rich) speaker companies, for research purposes. The walls, ceiling and floor are covered by materials which theoretically absorb all sounds of all frequencies, allowing *no* significant amount of reverberation. The T_{60} time is essentially zero. Music in such a room sounds as it would in the middle of a field, whereas our befuddled magazine editor is getting the sound he would have if he elected residence in the sewers of Paris. Neither place is a comfortable environment for listening to music.

finding the right reverb time

Then what *is* right? Obviously we need a compromise. We want a short T_{60} time, but we don't want it *infinitely* short. And we would probably like it to be about the same at all frequencies, though in fact this point is in dispute among acousticians. There is nothing wrong with using our confused friend's concrete room as a starting point, if only to spare the neighbors, but we will want to give it some sort of acoustical treatment. And since energy can be neither created nor destroyed, the energy that leaves the speakers can be gotten rid off in only one way: by turning it into some non-acoustical form of energy, probably heat. Let us see how we can go about doing this.

absorbing the highs

For high frequencies it is fairly easy. Most people know that carpeting and drapes are quite effective sound absorbers. So are "acoustic" tiles, which are soft and pillowy. At high frequencies such materials will drop the T_{60} time dramatically. Unfortunately this technique will not work at all frequencies. Lower frequency sound waves regard such materials as transparent, and they will pass through, bounce off the concrete or the gypsum board on the other side, and into the room again. Some thicker materials, including sofas and human beings, can absorb sound rather further down the band, but none of them are effective at low frequencies, and they are scarcely better in the middle band, where most musical information is located. It is common for amateur acousticians (and some pros who should know better) to fill a room with soft materials. The result is an extremely short T_{60} time at the high end, and a bottom end T_{60} time that is nearly as long as when the room was empty. Such a room sounds muffled because the highs are muted, but at the same time the bass reverberation creates aural confusion which makes it impossible to distinguish musical detail...or any other detail.

absorbing the lows

Absorbing very low frequencies is unfortunately not easy. Several companies sell devices to help treat rooms for better acoustics. There is a foam tile with a sculptured 3-D pattern, which can be glued on the wall. Community radio stations often use this in their studios, as do cable TV services. The 3-D pattern increases the surface of each tile, so that it absorbs more than a flat tile would, but the problem remains the same: it absorbs *only* high frequencies. There are cheaper ways to absorb highs, which is not a difficult job anyway. There are also round and semi-round absorbers, the best known of which go under the trade name *Tube Traps*. The large *Tube Traps* are quite helpful, with absorbing power that reaches below 1 kHz. The smaller tubes, however, are like other "acoustical" materials: they absorb highs and little else.

bass traps

Professionally-designed studios use a far more effective device to absorb lows: the bass trap. Behind a wall there is a large resonant cavity, covered by a thin but rigid membrane, easily penetrated by sound. The low waves enter the cavity, which resonates. The cavity is stuffed by mineral wool (typically Fiberglass), and the friction of the air against the fibers turns the sound energy into heat. A good studio will include a number of bass traps in different parts of the room, in differing sizes, so that each will

180

resonate at a different frequency. Bass traps are excellent low frequency absorbers, at least if they are deep enough. Unfortunately they must be constructed, and cannot simply be ordered from a parts catalog.

making a bass trap

Still, they are not difficult to build. Along one wall, mount a series of 2x4 studs, with the "four inch" (10 cm) side facing out. Fill the space with mineral wool, and cover it with prefinished wood panelling. Masonite can also be used, and either painted or faced with decorative cloth. A few of the spaces (not all) can be covered with perforated Masonite, which also allows some penetration (and absorption) of higher frequencies. Masonite is less likely to resonate audibly than wood panelling. Best of all for this task is asbestos panelling, but asbestos has had a bad press in recent years, and this once popular acoustical material is difficult to find.

Alternately, large boxes, a few centimeters deep, faced with thin panelling, can be hung on the wall. Such resonators have the advantage of being movable, and they are a good choice if you don't own your own home.

calculations

A really good listening room would have a set of absorbers whose surface was mathematically calculated to yield a given absorption at different frequencies. A knowledgeable architect can do precisely this sort of calculation for you. That is how our magazine listening room was built. This can be costly, however, and most people will go for a little more approximation than that.

acoustical theories

It is believed by some acousticians that T_{60} time should not be the same for all frequencies, that a shorter time in the highs will tame the harshness of most speakers, and that on the other hand a longer T_{60} time in the lows will yield a richer and deeper sound. Indeed building rooms in that fashion was the norm at one time, and for good reason. For one

Chapter 9: Installing it

thing, absorbing highs was all too easy, whereas absorbing lows was difficult. For another, the poor audio sources of that day sounded harsh, and sounded at the very least less offensive is the high end was cut down to size. On the other hand many speakers have a little difficulty reproducing very low frequencies, and a little extra reverb time seems to help...but not too much!

bottom end reverb

Yes...it *seems* to help. The extra "richness" at the bottom end is an illusion however. Room resonance stores energy, remember, and that energy returns slightly later to augment the newer signal from the speaker. This works with the steady-state tones used in testing, because one tone cycle is exactly like the preceding one, but it *doesn't* work with music, which is constantly changing. It is true that bass tones change relatively slowly, but even a 20 Hz tone can change in 0.05 second, and its second harmonic in only 0.025 second. A room which has a T_{60} time of 1.5 second will smear the sound hopelessly, confusing new information with old data.

small room, short reverb

It should be noted that, the smaller the room, the shorter must be its reverberation time. When we designed our listening room, our model was a large concert hall, whose T_{60} time at midband was well over 2 seconds. In those two seconds, the sound had time to cross the width of the hall four times. Our room is much smaller of course, and in two seconds the sound could have crossed it many more times. In order to get the *same* number of crossings, we had to hold the T_{60} time to only 0.22 second. Which is what we did.

In a room with well-controlled reverberation, music will be much clearer, with the subtleties of space and instrumental timbre much more apparent. It will even be more pleasant to talk in, with a warm and inviting ambience. Acoustical treatment is worth the trouble.

Soundproofing

This section will be short, because the news is mostly bad. Most homes *cannot* be soundproofed by any means whatsoever. That is because neighbors mostly share common structures: floors, walls and ceilings. Once the vibrations are in the structure, they will be heard. There is nothing to be done.

avoiding structure-borne sound

You *can* possibly keep sound out of the structure, by not firmly attaching loudspeakers to the main structure of the building, but this is not always possible. The backup solution is to raze the building and to have it rebuilt by a competent architect who knows something about sound.

soundproofing materials

In a few buildings, however, your neighbors can hear you directly through a wall rather than by conduction of sound through the structure. It is possible to soundproof such a wall, but it must be done with massive material, not soft "acoustic" tiles...which can actually *increase* transmission slightly! An excellent material, available from companies that manufacture metal in rolls, is sheet lead. A 0.4 mm sheet of lead has the same sound-stopping power as 4 cm thick plywood. However the plywood would become acoustically transparent at its resonant frequency; lead won't resonate at audible frequencies. Lead is expensive, however, and its isn't always effective. The smallest leak in the barrier will make it utterly useless.

Making a good listening room is unfortunately not much easier than making a good amplifier. But the result can be as gratifying. And it can make the music you hear much more enjoyable.

Improving It

Perhaps you already have a high fidelity system...a real one, not a famous-name mid-fi system. But now you'd like to improve it. Only how? Where do you begin? There is no subject that brings us more mail.

The order of improvements

Nearly all the information you need is in the previous chapters. The source is the most important part of a high fidelity system. Unless your source is truly excellent, improve it rather than changing the electronics or the loudspeakers.

the three parts of
the turntable
system

Things are a little more complex with analog sources, since turntables can be broken up into three distinct pieces: the turntable proper, the tone arm, and the phono pickup. That is the order of importance, by the way. There is no point on buying an ultra-rigid arm if the frame of your turntable can flex freely. There is no point in buying a cartridge that can resolve very fine detail if the tone arm has "play" in the bearings that is greater than the detail you are seeking to resolve.

think big

If you can, avoid making small improvements. We presume you will sell your old equipment, and inevitably you will take a beating on it. If the upgrade is going to cost you serious money, make sure it is worthwhile. If you're going to move from an entry-level turntable to the finest money can buy, it is better to do it in one or two steps than in three or four. Each trade costs money.

don't make it an
orphan

On the other hand, you should look carefully at the trade-in value of your components. If you have a low-cost arm and turntable, you *could* potentially improve the system by getting a new turntable and putting your arm on it. But that will leave your old turntable with no arm. Is it so desirable that someone will want it that way? If not, it is best to save your money a short while longer and change the turntable and tone arm together. And maybe the pickup as well. Equipment is *much* easier to sell if it is in plug-in-and-play condition. The cheaper the gear, the more that is true.

upgrading a CD player

At first glance it would appear that CD players cannot be upgraded a bit at a time, since they are mostly integrated boxes. In fact, however, the trend in high-end audio is to two-piece players. Part one is the mechanism, which has the laser and the digital circuits. The output is digital, and it may be a conventional coaxial cable *or* a fiber optic link, which carries signal in the form of light. Part two is the decoder, which turns the digital information into two analog audio channels. Several companies sell these two-piece players, which can be thought of as the digital counterpart of the turntable and preamplifier. And just as with these traditional components, the transport and decoder can be mixed and matched between brands.

But that isn't all. Most modern CD players now have digital outputs: usually a single phono jack labelled "digital." And so you can upgrade by stages, just as you can with analog components. You can begin with a moderately-priced player, then add a decoder to it, and finally sell the player and buy the transport.

will a decoder improve the sound?

This may or may not give you better sound, actually. Our chapter on digital sound outlines the reason many CD players sound so harsh: the mechanism is so poorly-made that it can barely recover the code from the disc. A *really* poor player has serious mechanical problems, and a new decoder won't save it. In any case you should consider such an upgrade to be an interim step, a way of improving your system without buying everything at once.

upgrading
electronics

Many audiophiles also improve their electronics a step at a time. If you already own a separate amplifier and preamplifier, then it's easy. You change the one that will make the most difference. If your main source is an analog turntable, that should be the preamplifier. If you listen mainly to CD, it should be the power amplifier.

what about an
integrated amp?

But what if you have an *integrated* amplifier? You can still upgrade piecemeal. Want a new preamplifier? Plug its output into one of the integrated amp's high level inputs (such as tuner or CD), and use the old amp as a power amp. Want a new power amplifier? That may be more difficult. However some integrated amplifiers have preamplifier outputs which allow you to use them as preamplifiers, and some others have provisions for conversion. Check the instruction manual, or ask your dealer.

speakers last

For reasons we've already explained, the loudspeakers should come last in the upgrade, unless your system is already excellent. Good speakers can transform your system, but they cannot remove distortion that originates upstream, nor can they replace missing audio information.

beyond simple
improvements

What happens if, ultimately, your system is *so* good you're not sure how to improve it further? There are improvements beyond the obvious. In this chapter we will discuss two of them.

Biamplification
by Gerard Rejskind

This is a way around the problems that a conventional crossover network causes in a loudspeaker. The highs and the lows are divided up at low level by an active filtering system known as an *electronic crossover* (so-called because it uses electronic devices like transistors, and not merely capacitors and coils). Separate amplifiers then feeds the woofers and the tweeters.

To see exactly how it works, look at the design of a conventional (passive) electronic crossover network, a simple one built with a coil and a capacitor.

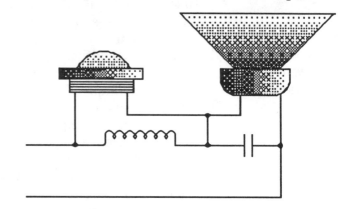

And now contrast that with a setup which includes an electronic crossover. Note the presence of two power amplifiers.

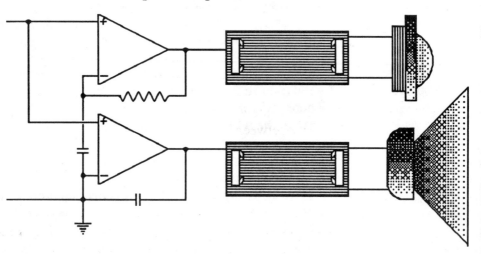

Except for cost and complexity, biamplification offers only advantages. Though it is certainly possible to design a low-level crossover that messes up phase and causes transient distortion, a competent designer can make one that is nearly perfect. There is then nothing between the amplifier and the woofer to interfere with tight control of cone motion by the amp. Many forms of intermodulation distortion (interaction between tones of different frequency) vanish entirely, since the highs and the lows never mix after the preamplifier. Woofers and tweeters of vastly different acoustical outputs can be readily mated.

who biamplifies

Biamplification is one of those phenomena that is at once well-known and poorly-known. It is best known in the professional world. Studio monitors are standardly biamplified. It is also widely used (for a different reason) in automobile audio. In home high fidelity, however, it is a rarity. There are reasons for this, but it is an option worth looking into if you are thinking about upgrading an expensive system.

biamplification in the studio

Biamplification is used in recording studios for a different reason. Most studio monitors are not necessarily what you could call high fidelity, but they are nonetheless very high-performance systems. They have very wide, flat frequency response, with linear phase, and exceptional transient response. They will have such performance at any power level, and I mean *any* power level! It is difficult to achieve such performance with a conventional crossover network placed between the amplifier and the woofer.

I must admit to being an old biamping freak. In my early days I actually reconverted from stereo back to mono, just so my two amplifiers would be free to biamplify my speakers. The change was worthwhile. When I once again had a full stereo system (not long after), I had six amplifiers, in a triamplified setup. I used it for many years, and I still own a triamplified system today.

What differences did I notice? Well, essentially there were two. First, I was finally able to match my woofer and tweeter together. The tweeter, a separately-purchased electrostatic model, was far less loud than the twin large-magnet woofers, and there was no way to jury-rig a conventional crossover network to make them sound right with just one amplifier. With a biamped system, it was a matter of turning up the volume a bit on the tweeter.

higher quality

The other difference was one of quality. Removing the passive crossover network made a dramatic difference. The woofers had always sounded rather loose and wooly. Suddenly they were tight and well-controlled. More detail could be heard, including very low-pitched sounds such as footfalls and traffic.

Now I don't want to claim too much for this system, which also had flaws apparent even to casual listeners. I did not have an electronic crossover of the quality available today, and I had to design my own. The phase relationship between the woofer and tweeter wasn't right, and frequency response was grossly inaccurate. But the system was good enough to demonstrate the potential of biamplification.

the advantages

The use of multiple amplifiers includes numerous advantages, but it also includes some notable disadvantages of which you should be aware. First the advantages.

(1) *Reduced intermodulation distortion.* As you probably know, intermodulation results from the interaction of two frequencies in the same device. If the highs and lows are amplified separately, they cannot interact to produce intermodulation. Most good power amplifiers have quite low IM in fact, but that isn't true of conventional crossovers.

(2) *Easy level matching.* Woofers and tweeters don't necessarily come perfectly matched for level. If it is the tweeter that needs extra volume — as very often happens — the conventional solution is to use a resistance network to knock the woofer's level down a little. This effectively isolates the woofer

more
advantages...

from the amplifier, and prevents it from controlling cone motion. More on this in a moment.

(3) *Easier phase matching*. With an electronic crossover operating at low level, all filtering can be done with capacitors and amplifier modules, whereas conventional crossovers are built with capacitors and inductors (coils). These two elements introduce frequency-dependent delay, with the result that sounds that left the amplifier in step will emerge from the speakers out of step. The same problem can exist in an electronic crossover, but it is easier to avoid.

(4) *Much better woofer damping*. Let me explain this. You probably know that most transistor amplifiers are rated at 8 ohms, and are intended to drive 8Ω speakers. However the internal impedance of a typical amplifier is not 8Ω. It may in fact be closer to 0.1Ω. Now here is what happens. A signal from the amplifier sets the woofer cone in motion. The woofer behaves as though it were an electric motor, but at the same time it also acts like an electrical *generator*. The motion generates a "back voltage" which is opposite in polarity to the amplifier signal. This voltage is virtually shorted out, however, because of the amplifier's very small 0.1Ω impedance. With the back voltage shorted, the cone motion is braked, and it stops moving. This is highly desirable. The amplifier's signal gets the speaker moving, and its low impedance stops the motion again so it doesn't go on flapping. This is called damping the speaker cone, and when you divide the speaker impedance (8 ohms) by the amplifier impedance (0.1 ohm), you get the damping factor...which in this case is 80.

but...

However this scenario assumes that there isn't a resistance lurking between the speaker and the amplifier, such as a bad cable, a poor connector, or the elements of a crossover network. Eliminating the

190

crossover greatly improves the amplifier's ability to control the woofer cone.

the drawbacks
And now the disadvantages. There are more of them than there are advantages, and they may be enough to prevent you from envisaging biamplification.

(1) *High cost.* There's no way around this. Electronic crossover networks are very expensive, and you'll also need a second amplifier. You can get by with a much less powerful amplifier for the high frequencies, but you'll want a very good one... otherwise what's the point?

Naturally the cost gets higher yet if you're thinking about triamplification.

(2) *The difficulty of finding a suitable crossover.* Most crossovers sold are designed for sound reinforcement applications, and they are not high fidelity. They will make a system sound worse, not better. If you do find a good one, it may not operate at the crossover frequency you need.

(3) *Increased distortion* from the addition of another component. This will be true even if you get the best crossover in the world. You are adding extra amplification, extra capacitors (of what quality?), extra cables, extra connectors, and extra volume controls. You'll need a major sonic improvement to make up for all that stuff.

(4) *The need to modify loudspeakers* for biamplification. A few loudspeakers are designed to be used with an electronic crossover, but of course most are not. If that's the case with yours, you'll have to cut them open, remove the existing crossover, and rewire the system. You will then have to reseal the enclosure to the manufacturer's standard. I wouldn't blame you if your hands shook a little as you did this.

By the way, some "biamplification-ready" speakers have extra connectors which leave the regular crossover in place even if you biamplify. You'll get *some* of the advantages of biamplification, but of course you won't get them all.

(5) *Unpredictability.* With nearly any other improvement you can make to your system, you can listen to the improvement at a good store first. That isn't true of biamplification.

(6) *Violation of the speaker design.* If your speakers are any good, the manufacturer has spent a great deal of time and money working out its configuration. As an example, think about why the woofer and tweeter are placed physically as they are. In many cases, it will be to compensate for the phase shift introduced by the crossover network. What happens if you remove that crossover and introduce an electronic one with different phase shift?

(7) *The difficulty of balancing* a biamplified system. I hate loudspeakers which have a "brightness knob," a volume control for the tweeter. It suggests the speaker designer had no idea of what the frequency balance of the speaker should be, and so he's leaving it to you to complete the design for him. Well, that's exactly what a biamplified system is. Getting the output of the woofer and tweeter right is a major task that essentially requires the same test facilities you'd find in a good speaker research lab. Doing it by ear is not as good.

I still believe in biamplification and triamplification, because I have heard the dramatic difference they can make. I wish more manufacturers would provide at least biamplification as a factory-recommended (and implemented) upgrade path, making the procedure easier, more predictable and relatively risk-free. Until they do, you are taking a risk. You can make your system sound much better, or — if you get things wrong — you can make it unlistenable. Look before you leap.

What's even better than biamplification?

Triamplification, that's what. More complexity. Still more money. A lot more cables. But the payoff is major…if the system is designed right, of course.

no free lunch

Biamping and triamping aside, nearly every alternative speaker technology involves tradeoffs. You gain over here, and you lose over there. And sometimes you get new problems you didn't anticipate. That's why most speakers are still made with 1920's technology.

What's sure is that, no matter what technology you use, there can be no substitute for good design.

Subwoofers
by Paul Bergman

the search for bass

Lack of bass is one of the most common complaints of audiophiles. They want to feel the impact of the drums, the thump of the tympani, the plucking of the bass, the pedal of the pipe organ. Ordinary loudspeakers of the type most commonly used at home will simply not reproduce those very low sounds, nor can they be expected to. It is not surprising, therefore, that so many audiophiles think of adding a subwoofer to their systems.

why many speakers have thin bass

I should add that designers of domestic loudspeaker systems often deliberately sacrifice bass response. This would not be acceptable to professional users, who require full-range reproduction, but audiophiles generally have other priorities. It may be instructive to look at what these priorities might be, and why they are not altogether compatible with extended low-frequency response.

the virtues of simplicity

It is now recognized that loudspeakers with many drivers are for the most part not high fidelity products. There are exceptions to this, as there are to nearly everything, but it can generally be said that true hi-fi speakers are marked by simplicity of design. At most they will have three drivers — a woofer, midrange and tweeter — and even some quite expensive speakers have only two. Having just two drivers offers considerable advantages. The crossover network is simplified, and is less likely to interfere with the amplifier-speaker relationship. There is less distortion, since considerable intermodulation distortion is generated at each crossover point. More importantly, perhaps, the crossover point is likely to be around 1.5 kHz to 2 kHz, instead of right about middle C, where the ear is most sensitive. Finally, crossover networks create errors in phase between drivers, and one such error is better than two.

good speakers have a hard time

However covering the range with only two drivers is not easy. Any tweeter that will reproduce higher frequencies comfortably will almost certainly have a very small diaphragm. That means it will not be able to go down very low in frequency, and it will be necessary to cross over to the woofer at a relatively high frequency. That in turn means that the woofer will have to reproduce most of the audible range, something a very large woofer cannot do. Its heavy cone is not maneuverable enough to reproduce midrange transient sounds accurately. For that reason it will be fairly small, probably around 20 cm in diameter.

This is smaller than the woofer you'll find even in a moderate-sized *JBL* monitor, for instance. The chances are that it will not go down very far into the low frequencies. Unless the cabinet is exceptionally large, it will begin to roll off around 80 Hz, and the rolloff might well be quite rapid. One octave down (at 40 Hz) it will produce mostly noise, if it produces anything at all.

I must emphasize once more that this rolloff is the result of *deliberate choices* made by the speaker designer. It is possible to have an extra octave or two at the bottom end even with a moderately-sized speaker, but it cannot be done without sacrificing some other aspect of performance.

bass response
may mean nothing

I should add one other detail, which may turn out to be the key to this discussion. Frequency response in itself is not as meaningful as it appears to be. Even a small speaker can be made to reproduce very low frequencies at what engineers call "small signal levels." Small, in this case, may mean very small indeed, and that is the problem of many domestic speakers. They may (possibly) be able to reproduce a frequency of 40 Hz, but they can do it only at a barely audible level. At increased levels they may suffer from distortion that can actually pass the 80% level!

extending
headroom

The subwoofer is often more useful in overcoming that problem than in extending frequency response. It is adding, in the jargon of the audio engineer, bass headroom.

This is the case of more and more subwoofers. At one time, subwoofers were intended to reproduce (as the name more or less suggests) subsonic signals, below 30 Hz or so. Adding such a device to an analog disc reproducing system was rather courageous, since much of its output was of machine-made noises, but such subwoofers flourished for a time. Some of them were designed around the *Electro-Voice* 76 cm woofer, a breathtaking beast that could move enough air to snuff the candles on quite an elderly person's birthday cake. It was frequently placed in a closet, giving it the possibility of reaching all the way down to 16 Hz, which is the pitch of a 32 foot organ pipe.

today's
subwoofers

I have not seen (or felt!) such a subwoofer for some years, however, and more recent ones have had less ambitious missions. They cross over (i.e. take over the work) at a frequency of 100 Hz, or even 200 Hz.

That 200 Hz frequency is a crucial one, because there is a study showing that below 200 Hz experimental subjects cannot identify the source of a sound. Thus (so goes the audio designer's corollary) you can have a single woofer for both channels operating from 200 Hz down. So well known is the study that many subwoofers are actually crossed over at that magic 200 Hz frequency. This might well be a good choice if crossover points were absolute, but in fact transitions between speakers occur gradually over a certain range of frequencies. I have seen a subwoofer crossing over at 200 Hz with a crossover slope of 6 dB/octave. In practical terms, this means that the woofer is down by the usual 3 dB at 200 Hz, by 9 dB at 400 Hz, by 15 dB at 800 Hz, and so on. It will be quite audible as a distinct source of sound. You can see the problem in this graph, which shows the frequency bands covered by the subwoofer and the main speaker.

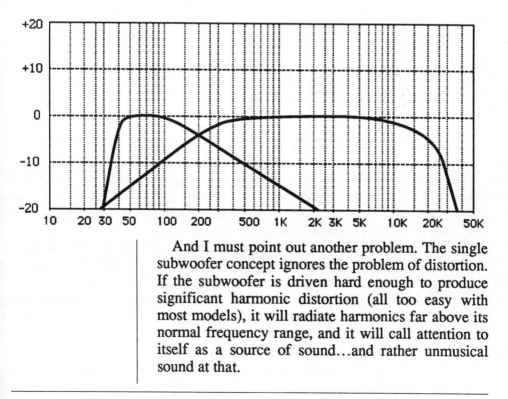

And I must point out another problem. The single subwoofer concept ignores the problem of distortion. If the subwoofer is driven hard enough to produce significant harmonic distortion (all too easy with most models), it will radiate harmonics far above its normal frequency range, and it will call attention to itself as a source of sound...and rather unmusical sound at that.

It is obvious from looking at most of today's sub-woofers that they are not designed to reproduce 32 foot organ pedals. Rather they are used to boost headroom at the relatively low frequencies which are still within the regular speaker's range. However it cannot possibly do this successfully unless the regular speaker is prevented from operating within that band.

Let me supply a concrete example. You have, let us say, a medium-sized speaker whose response extends down to 45 Hz, but cannot supply much volume below 150 Hz. You add a subwoofer, crossing over at 150 Hz, which extends down to 40 Hz. This is not much better than the main speaker, but of course the subwoofer can reproduce those lower frequencies at much greater loudness. Now let us say that you listen to a recording which contains a saxophone note of 75 Hz. What happens?

If the main speaker is still carrying the full range of frequencies, it will also try to reproduce the note, but because of its poor performance in that part of the band, it will generate a great deal of harmonic distortion. True, you will have added some "real" 75 Hz fundamental with the subwoofer, but the sound will be nearly as harsh as it was before. For that reason, the main speaker must be prevented from operating in the lower range.

Now let us say that in fact there is a crossover network of sorts to accomplish exactly that. You plug the amplifier into the subwoofer, and the subwoofer then feeds the main speaker. It will, in all likelihood, have a capacitor in series with the main speaker feed, to filter out the lows. The capacitor will allow response to fall at 6 dB per octave. The main speaker will then be, as in the earlier example, 3 dB down at 150 Hz, and 9 dB down at 75 Hz. The question is: will it now misbehave if it is called upon to produce 9 dB less sound than before? It still may, though it is bound to distort less, and of course its distortion products will be 9 dB lower as well. Whether this is good enough is another question. It is preferable to have a rather sharper slope, perhaps as sharp as 18 dB/octave. That would drop the main speaker's response by 21 dB at the 75 Hz mark, certainly enough to keep it out of trouble. Even so, it will be at nearly full level at 150 Hz, and it may not behave exceptionally well at that frequency either.

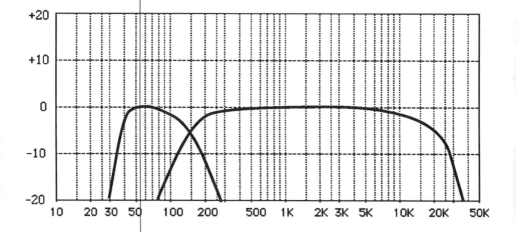

The addition of a subwoofer, then, is a compromise with possible undesirable consequences. It is a method for turning a two-way loudspeaker system into a three-way system, but without the benefit of a single manufacturer's engineering knowhow. It is in general far more desirable to select a speaker which has sufficiently good performance that it does not need a subwoofer. If that cannot be arranged, you should select a subwoofer which (a) has very high power bandwidth, so that it will not produce spurious harmonics under any reasonable circumstances, (b) crosses over at a relatively low frequency, preferably 100 Hz if the main speaker can handle the band down to that frequency, and (c) incorporates a should you do it?

sharp-slope crossover network, preferably an electronic one.

Even so, you may not be happy with the results unless your main loudspeakers have sufficient low-frequency performance in the first place. You should, finally, examine the price of the proposed system (the subwoofer, plus the extra amplifier to drive it if it needs one, minus the resale value of your main speakers), and compare it to the purchase price of a speaker system that does what you wish without adding on anything.

The Future

Will high fidelity continue to improve? Yes, but that doesn't mean you should flock to the almost monthly "improvements" trumpeted in the magazines. It is significant that the *Quad* II, a tube power amplifier first introduced in 1951, is still avidly sought, not just by collectors, but by *audiophiles* who want to use them in their systems! Talk to *those* people about "progress."

real progress

But of course there *has* been progress. Turntables from 1951 seem terrible today, as do those from 1961 and even 1971. The quality of audio sources has increasd tremendously, and we believe that will continue. Certainly CD players are improving, as is the quality of the discs themselves. And the development of a very few expensive landmark players has demonstrated that much more can be done yet.

fewer LP's, better turntables

At the same time, with the gradual disappearance of analog discs from the mid-fi world, turntables will continue to improve because they will have to. Why bother with the inconvenience and the technical flaws of analog unless you're going to wring every drop of quality from it?

not many breakthroughs coming

We are *not* so sure there are breakthroughs around the corner in electronics and in loudspeakers. Some very good new designs will no doubt emerge, but we'd expect them to be the result of extra care in design and construction, not of a fundamental breakthrough in technology. We don't want to seem unduly cynical, but a lot of "breakthroughs" turn out to be mere fads. Is there an exception on the horizon? We shall see.

A lot of already pretty good products will improve, however. The discoveries of some high-end designers (that it pays to use good parts, for instance) are filtering down to the makers of lower-cost gear. That will be beneficial for those of us who have limited budgets. At the same time, mass-market products can be expected to become worse, as the international giants slash prices in order to gain competitive advantage, and therefore eliminate everything that can't be seen from the outside. The schism between mid-fi and hi-fi can only grow.

We don't dare to get more prophetic than that, because we are aware that a book — unlike a magazine — has a long shelf life! Foretelling the future is a dangerous game.

hi-fi lives

But we're convinced of one thing. Whatever fads and gadgets come and go in the electronic marketplace, there will always be people who think that music is one of the great pleasures of life. There will always be people who take refuge in good music when all else is going wrong.

We will be among them, and if you've read all the way to the end we think you will be too.

Together, we will shape the future of high fidelity.

Appendix A:
The Jargon

**A lexicon of the terms used in this book
and in *Ultra High Fidelity Magazine.***

A/D converter: A converter which converts analog (conventional) signals to digital code. Used in the making of Compact Discs and other digital recordings.

AC: Alternating current. The power company supplies AC to your home, and audio is also made up of AC. Alternating current reverses constantly in voltage, 120 times per second in the case of household current, at different rates in the case of audio.

Aggressive: An adjective sometimes used to describe sound that is annoyingly bright. Such sounds seems to have excessive treble, though in fact it may not.

Acoustic suspension: An innovative speaker design invented in the 1950's, which yields considerable bass from a small cabinet. The woofer has a very soft, compliant suspension barely stiff enough to hold the cone in place. The cone is then held up by the stiffness of the air in a small, sealed cabinet. Acoustic suspension speakers are less popular than they were, because they are inefficient: they require exceptionally powerful amplifiers to drive them.

Active: Said of a circuit which uses amplification devices, like transistors or vacuum tubes. As opposed to *passive*.

Analog: A representation of information which is *analogous* to the information itself. For instance, sound can be represented by an alternating current, or by an undulating groove in a record.

Both are analogs of the sound. By contrast, *digital* representations contain only data about the information, and do not resemble the original information itself.

Anechoic chamber: A special room whose walls and other boundaries are designed to absorb all sound. Such a room allows a design engineer to study the behavior of a device such a loudspeaker, without having to take room reverberation into account.

Amplifier stage: A section of an amplifier, consisting of one or more transistors, integrated circuits, or vacuum tubes. For convenience, an amplifier can be spoken of as having different stages.

Amplitude: Magnitude. Mainly said of audio signals.

Baffle: Today, a synonym for the cabinet of a loudspeaker. Originally a baffle was a rather simple cabinet, often no more than a face plate in which a loudspeaker could be mounted. It "baffled" the sound from the rear so that it didn't come around and cancel out the sound from the front. Such baffles are now rare, but the word is still with us.

Balance control: A knob which adjusts the volume of one stereo channel in relation to the other. Such a control is convenient if you are listening from a position other than the centre of the room, or if the original source has one channel louder than the other.

Bandwidth: A band of frequencies. This term is often used in reference to specific equipment. For instance, if an amplifier can adequately amplify all signals between the frequencies of 10 Hz and 50 kHz, it can be said to have a *bandwidth* of 10 Hz to 50 kHz. More rarely, it will simply be said to have a bandwidth of 50 kHz.

Bass reflex: A common speaker design method. A hole is placed in the cabinet, sometimes with a tube attached to it, which will resonate at a specific frequency. By the Helmholtz resonator method, taught in high school physics, the back wave of the speaker will be reversed in phase: it will push instead of pulling and vice versa. Bass reflex speakers are difficult to tune correctly, and sound awful if they're not, but they are popular because they require relatively less amplifier power.

Belt drive: A method of coupling a turntable to its motor: an elastic band is placed around the platter and around the motor pulley.

Most genuine high fidelity turntables are belt-driven.

Binary: A counting method which uses only ones and zeroes instead of the digits from 0 to 9. Computer and digital audio circuits use binary arithmetic for the same reason we would if we had only one figure on each hand. A transistor circuit in a computer can only be on (one) or off (zero).

Bit: Short for BInary digIT. The "words" used in digital audio are made up of 16 bits.

Bridging: A method for using a stereo amplifier as though it were a much more powerful mono amplifier. In bridged mode, each of the stereo channels is used to amplify half the sound wave. Bridging is accomplished by a special circuit which is usually (but not always) inside the amplifier itself.

Burst error: In digital audio, a large error which loses so much data that the missing values cannot be guessed, or even approximated, by looking at the adjacent data, which is also gone. Burst errors can be catastrophic, and modern digital recordings are made with special techniques to allow recovery from burst errors.

Cantilever: The small lever which emerges from the bottom of a phono pickup, and which has the stylus mounted on the end. The cantilever is usually made of aluminum, but on some esoteric cartridges it can be made of beryllium, ruby, or even diamond.

Capacitor: An electronic part which has the property known (naturally) as capacitance. One can make a capacitor by placing two large plates close together, so that they nearly touch. Such capacitors would be cumbersome, and so the two plates are rolled up into a cylinder. The short gap between them is usually filled, not with air, but with some dielectric material, such as polystyrene, or — in the best capacitors — polypropylene.

Capstan: A rotating metal shaft which determines the speed of the tape in a tape deck. Opposite the capstan there is usually a *pinch roller*. Together, the two squeeze the tape along at a controlled speed.

Cartridge: A common term for a phono pickup.

Checksum: A simple method of error detection used in some digital circuits, including those of Compact Discs. The 16th digit of the digital word is the checksum. It is a one or a zero, depending on whether the number of ones in the rest of the word is odd or even. If the checksum is inconsistent with the rest of the data, the error-correction circuit knows there is an error and can then attempt to correct it.

Chip: A common word for an integrated circuit, since it is made using a chip of silicon material. An integrated circuit, also known as an IC, may contain dozens or even millions of transistors.

Class A: A mode of amplifier operation, in which all transistors (or tubes) function constantly, even when they are not amplifying anything. The transistors of a class B amplifier, by contrast, operate only when they are needed, namely exactly half the time. In a class AB amplifier (which most hi-fi amplifiers are), the transistors or tubes operate more than half the time, but not constantly.

Coaxial cable: A type of cable used to connect different audio components, though usually not loudspeakers. In a "coax" cable, one wire is in the centre, and the other is a sheath, mounted *coaxially* around it. The sheath is grounded to the chassis of one or more of the units. It acts to shield the other conductor from electromagnetic fields and other sources of interference.

Comparator box: A device which allows a store to make instantaneous comparisons of different audio components (for instance, loudspeakers) by switching instantaneously among them. Stores with comparator boxes should be avoided.

Counterweight: A weight on the back of a tone arm. By adjusting the exact position of the counterweight, the pressure on the stylus, at the other end of the arm, can be increased or decreased.

Crossover network: A circuit which breaks audio signals up into different frequency bands (for instance: bass, midrange and treble) so that each can be sent to a speaker designed to reproduce that particular part of the band.

Crossover point: In a loudspeaker, the particular frequency where one driver (for instance the tweeter) begins to take over from another driver (for instance the woofer).

Current: The amount of flow of electricity. Measured in amperes or in fractions, such as milliamperes.

D/A converter: A device which converts digital information into analog (audio) signals. Such converters are an integral part of CD players, but are sometimes sold separately.

Damping: The action of resisting movement. For instance, the felt pad inside an automobile hood *damps* vibrations so that the hood doesn't ring like a bell. In the same way, damping materials may be used in loudspeakers, phono pickups, and other devices.

Damping factor: The ability of an amplifier to control the cone of a loudspeaker. It is determined by dividing the loudspeaker impedance (typically 8 ohms) by the internal impedance of the amplifier itself (nearly always well under 1 ohm).

DAT: Digital audio tape. This is the name of a cassette player which records using digits, by a process much like that of CD. It is sometimes called R-DAT...with "R" for *rotary,* because the tape heads are mounted on a spinning rotary drum, like those of a videocassette recorder.

DC: Direct current. Electricity which always flows in the same direction. In opposition to AC: alternating current. Oddly, both abbreviation are used even when the reference is to something other than current: for instance, "AC voltage," or "AC power."

Decibel: A logarithmic unit which is used to express ratios of loudness, voltage, power, etc. A change of 10 times in loudness or power — or 20 times in voltage — corresponds to 10 decibels. It is, by the way, meaningless to say that a stereo system can produce a volume of "106 dB." People who say this probably mean the dBa, another logarithmic unit, with an absolute value. A value of 0 dBa is considered to be the threshold of human hearing.

Digital: A method of counting using binary digits. Digital circuits operate only on data expressed in binary digits, and ignore all other signals.

Digital filter: A filter which operates on digital audio signals before they are reconverted to analog (audio) signals. Digital filters are commonly used on the output of CD players, to prevent digital pulses from getting into the audio.

DIN: A German agency which regulates industrial standards. The

DIN abbreviation is found in many domains, from vitamin bottles to audio measurement methods.

Direct drive: A method of turning the platter of a turntable, in which the platter is actually part of the motor. Direct drive turntables are highly reliable and quick to accelerate, but nearly all have too much vibration to be used in high fidelity.

Distortion: Any unwanted change in a signal. See *harmonic distortion, intermodulation distortion,* and *transient intermodulation distortion.*

Driver: A common name for one of the loudspeakers in a *speaker system,* which is composed of the drivers, the crossover, and the cabinet.

Dolby noise reduction: A highly-popular method of recording and playing back from magnetic tape — professional or domestic — with minimum noise. However the *Dolby* name is now widely used in association with processes that have nothing to do with noise reduction: Dolby HX Professional (used for headroom extension in tapes), and Dolby Surround (used in film and video sound).

Doppler distortion: A peculiar type of distortion found in small speakers which are called upon to reproduce heavy bass. The Doppler effect is what causes the sound of an approaching car to rise in pitch, and then drop in pitch after the car goes by. As a small speaker moves back and forth, toward and away from the listener, the higher pitched tones emitted by the same speaker are similarly shifted in pitch, upward and downward.

Dynamic range: This is the difference, expressed in decibels, between the loudest signal a system can reproduce or record, and the background noise.

Efficiency: The ability of a loudspeaker to turn electricity into sound, expressed as a percentage. If you put 100 watts of power into a typical speaker of 5% efficiency, you'll get 5 watts of sound and 95 watts of heat.

Electronic crossover: A crossover network using active components, which divides up frequencies before final amplification takes place. An electronic crossover requires one amplifier for every driver in the speaker system. See *crossover network, active,* and *driver.*

Equalization: A correction in the amplitude of frequencies so that they are as they should be. Equalization is performed on the signal from an LP or a cassette, since both are recorded with the high frequencies boosted in relation to the low frequencies. The term is often abused however. *Equalizers* are multi-band tone controls which are mostly used to make frequencies *unequal*. Though equalizers have their uses, they should not be used in high fidelity systems.

Feedback: A method of distortion reduction. A sample of an amplifier's output is brought back to the input, and allowed to partly cancel itself out, therefore reducing some forms of distortion. Feedback is a useful method that is too often abused.

Feedforward: Another distortion reduction method. A large amplifier and a smaller (presumably better) amplifier both amplify a signal. The output of the small one is then used to correct the output of the big one. Rarely used, though it can work well.

FET: Field effect transistor, a semiconductor device which works differently from conventional (bipolar) transistors. Like tubes, FET's have high impedance and can handle high voltages. They are sometimes used in high-quality audio amplifiers and preamplifiers.

Fiber optic: A plastic fibre with perfectly reflective internal sides, which can carry a light beam the way a hose carries water. In audio, fiber optics are sometimes used to carry digital signals among sections of CD players, because, unlike conventional electrical cable, fiber optics are immune to interference.

Flutter: A rapid wavering in the speed of a turntable or tape deck.

Frequency: Pitch. Frequency is measured in Hertz (which were once called "cycles per second"), or in multiples: kilohertz or megahertz. Abbreviated Hz, kHz and MHz respectively.

Frequency response: The ability to amplify or reproduce, with little or no deviation in level, different frequencies. A device with "good frequency response" can handle a signal of any frequency, or nearly so.

Gain: Amplification. Gain is expressed with unitless numbers. For instance, if you put a 1 volt signal into an amplifier, and there is a 10 volt signal at the output, then that amplifier has a voltage gain of 10.

208

Harmonics: Multiples of a "fundamental" frequency. Harmonics occur in nature: for instance a violin playing a note or 440 Hz will also produce harmonics of 880 Hz, 1760 Hz, and so on. However audio equipment may produce false harmonics, not all of which coincide with naturally-occurring harmonics.

Harmonic distortion: Distortion caused by the addition of extra harmonics of the original sound. Sometimes called *total harmonic distortion* (THD), the sum of all the spurious harmonics, expressed as a percentage of the original signal. For instance: *0.5% THD*.

Headshell: The end of a tone arm, in which the phono cartridge is mounted. In many tone arms the headshell is removable, which is convenient for mounting cartridges and for changing rapidly from one cartridge to the other. However removable headshells add unwanted mass and reduce rigidity, and for that reason the best arms have fixed headshells.

Hertz: A unit of frequency. Formerly called cycles per second (using that term marks you as an old timer!), and abbreviated Hz.

Idler: A bum. Oh yes — and also a rubber-tired wheel that couples the platter of a turntable to the shaft of the motor. Idler-driven turntables are terribly noisy and cannot be used in high fidelity.

Impedance: The property of a circuit of resisting the flow of current. It is to alternating current what *resistance* is to direct current. Both impedance and resistance are measured in ohms.

Inductance: A property of a coil, which is deliberately designed to have inductance. Small amounts of inductance are also found in other devices, including wire. Measured in Henries, or fractions of Henries.

Inductor: A coil, whose important property is inductance. An inductor behaves as though it were a resistor whose value varies with frequency. Useful in filters of all sorts.

Information: As used in high fidelity, any part of the signal which represents some aspect of the original sound. *Information loss* is the loss of any part of the signal, thereby reducing the ability to hear how the original music sounded.

Infrasonic: At a frequency below the threshold of hearing. Sometimes mistakenly called *subsonic* (which actually means travelling below the speed of sound).

Infrasonic filter: A filter which removes signals below the threshold of hearing (about 20 Hz). Such filters are sometimes included in phono preamplifiers, since LP's often contain large infrasonic signals, especially if they are warped. Such signals cannot be reproduced, but they may overload the amplifier or the speakers.

Integrated amplifier: An amplifier which contains, in a single box, a power amplifier and a preamplifier.

Integrated circuit: A tiny device containing a silicon chip, on which thousands or even millions of transistors and resistors can be etched. IC's are the key to low-cost audio, since a complete stereo preamplifier can be built on a chip that costs less than a dollar. They are indispensable to digital audio, since digital circuits require more transistors than can handily be accommodated in a conventional circuit. However audio IC's are not used in the best high fidelity equipment.

Intermodulation distortion: A distortion which manifests itself by the generation of sounds mathematically related to the original sound. For instance, if an amplifier with IM amplifies simultaneously sounds of 100 Hz and 1000 Hz, it will generate sounds equal to the sum and difference of the tones, namely 900 Hz and 1100 Hz.

Lateral tracking angle: In a turntable, the angle between the phono pickup and a line tangent to the groove at the point where the stylus is riding. That angle should of course be 0°, but most arms will have a small error at every point on the record except two.

Linear: Undistorted. A linear device is one in which the output is exactly proportional to the output, so that if you graphed the two, you would get a straight line. Non-linearities are departures from this perfection, and may represent different types of distortion.

Loudness: Sometimes a synonym for volume, loudness is also used to mean the *subjective perception* of loudness. In other words, volume can be measured with instruments, but loudness is only perceived by humans.

Mat: A disc of felt, rubber or other material which covers the platter of a turntable. A mat may damp the resonance of a metal platter, or it may damp those of the record itself. On the other hand a mat may reduce the rigidity of the overall record-playing system, and cause a loss of information.

Medite: Medium density board. A dense panel made of fine wood chips, commonly used for loudspeaker cabinets. Medite is denser than the common chipboard used in construction, but its lack of grain makes it less resonant than hardwood or even plywood.

Midrange: The middle of the audible frequency band, typically between 100 Hz and 8 kHz. Also used as shorthand for *midrange driver,* a speaker specifically intended to reproduce the middle of the band. Used with a woofer and a tweeter.

Microphonic: The property of devices other than microphones and phono pickups to turn vibrations into an electrical signal. If you hit an amplifier and you hear a sound emerge from the speaker, that amplifier is said to be microphonic. That is, of course, undesirable.

Modulation noise: A noise heard from magnetic tape which appears *only* when sound has been recorded. Usually caused by roughness in the tape, in the tape heads, or in some other mechanical parts.

MOSFET: Metal oxide semiconductor field effect transistor. See *FET.*

Moving coil pickup: A phono pickup in which the magnet is fixed in place, while the stylus causes a coil to vibrate in its magnetic field.

Moving magnet pickup: A phono pickup in which the coil is fixed in place, while the stylus causes a magnet to vibrate close to it.

Musicality: A subjective term used to evaluate high fidelity systems and parts of systems. It refers to the ability to reproduce a recording in such a way that its musical attributes (melody, harmony, rhythm, etc.) can be readily appreciated.

Muting: In an FM tuner, a circuit which shuts off the sound when no station is tuned, so that you don't hear interstation hiss. In Compact Disc playback, the player is said to *mute* if it can no longer make proper sense of the code from the disc, or if it loses its place on the disc. In other words, it shuts off the output.

Noise: In the broadest sense, noise is everything that is not signal. In practice, however, *distortion* is usually excluded from the definition of noise.

Non-linear: Distorted. See *linear*.

Oscilloscope: A test device with a TV-like screen which can display the shape of an audio (or video) signal. It allows direct visualization of what the signal is like.

Oversampling: A method used to reduce (or even eliminate) the filter at the output of a CD player, which causes phase shift. The problem is caused by the fact that the digital sampling circuits operate at 44.1 kHz, while the system must reproduce sound up to 20 kHz. The filter is used to keep them apart. In oversampling, each sample is repeated (let's say) four times, so that the sampling circuits now appear to operate at 176.4 kHz. This adds no new information, but a gentler (and less harmful) filter can be used. Some players use 16 times oversampling and require no filter at all.

Passive: Using no amplifying devices, such as transistors and tubes. As opposed to *active*.

Pentode: A vacuum tube using five elements: the plate, the cathode, and three grids.

Phase   The state of an alternating current compared to another alternating current. If the output of an amplifier is positive when its input is negative, and vice versa, then the two signals are said to be 180° out of phase with each other. Various devices can cause *phase shift*, throwing different signals, or different *parts* of signals, out of step with one another.

Pickup: A device used to get information from an analog record, also called a *cartridge*. Like a microphone, it can turn vibration into an electrical signal.

Play: A theatrical work. Also, looseness in a mechanical system. For instance, the pivot of a tone arm should allow the arm tube to rotate, and that is all. Any other movement (for instance, from side to side) is called play. Play is caused by loose bearings, whereas friction is caused by *tight* bearings. Sometimes you can't win for losing!

Port: A fine dessert wine, or a handy place to catch a boat. Also, the name given to the hole in the cabinet of a *bass reflex* speaker.

Power: Electrical energy. It should be noted that power is equal to voltage multiplied by current. So 10 volts at 1 ampere equals 10 watts, and 1 volt at 10 amperes also equals 10 watts.

Power amplifier: A unit which can amplify a signal of (approximately) two volts so that it is large enough to move the cone of a loudspeaker.

Power supply: An electrical transformation device, usually part of an amplifier, though power supplies are found in other equipment as well. A power supply takes 120 volts AC (the common household current found in North America), and transforms it into one or more DC voltages that can be used by the device.

Preamplifier: The amplifying device that comes before the *power amplifier*. The preamp commonly has switches that allow the selection of different inputs, and other controls, such as a volume control. It commonly also includes a circuit which allows the amplification and equalization of the feeble signal from a phono pickup.

Pre-preamplifier: Yet another box that may come before the preamp, to amplify the *very* feeble signal from a moving coil pickup. The pre-preamp may be incorporated in the preamp itself, or "may be purchased separately," as they say in toy stores.

Resonance: The natural tendency of any mechanical or electrical device to vibrate at a given frequency. Both electrical and mechanical resonances are of concern in high fidelity. Note that sometimes a speaker cabinet, say, will be referred to as "non-resonant." In fact *everything* is resonant. However the panel may have its resonance at a frequency other than those likely to be reproduced by the speaker, and it may be highly *damped,* so that it doesn't go on resonating after it has been "excited" by some energy force.

Quantizing noise: Noise added in the process of turning a conventional analog signal into a digital representation of that signal. Quantizing noise is unavoidable. For that reason it is undesirable to move a high fidelity signal in and out of the digital domain more than once.

Receiver: An all-in-one electronic device which includes amplifier, preamplifier, and (typically) AM/FM tuner. Very few receivers are high fidelity, though there is an occasional exception.

Reed-Solomon code: The code by which digital signals are recorded on a Compact Disc. The Reed-Solomon system is intended to allow a CD system to perform well even if there are many errors in data recovery, which is unfortunately nearly always the case.

Reactance: A catch-all word which refers to both inductance and capacitance, and sometimes both. For instance, a wirewound resistor, which is made by winding resistive wire around a ceramic core, can be said to have not only resistance, but reactance as well.

Rectifier: A device which allows electricity to flow in one direction but not in the other. This may be a vacuum tube (rare today) or a semiconductor diode. It allows the transformation of AC into DC, and is an essential part of a *power supply*.

Resistance: The tendency of a device to resist the flow of a direct current. Measured in ohms. In the case of alternating current, the word *impedance* is used.

Resistor: An electronic part which has a carefully calibrated resistance, and can be inserted in a circuit.

Reverberation: Usually called "echo" in common language, it is the bouncing of sound from surface to surface of a room. *Reverberation time* (sometimes abbreviated T_{60}) is the time required after a sound is shut off until the sound dies away to 60 decibels (one million times) below the original volume.

RIAA equalization: A standard curve used to record and play back analog records. Highs are boosted and lows are lowered during recording, and then the reverse is done during playback. That allows the highs to override the predominantly high-pitched record noise, and it prevents the lows from causing excessively large excursions of the groove. There used to be several competing equalization curves. The dominant one is that of the *Record Industry Association of America.*

Root mean square: Maximum value multiplied by the square root of two. In the case of an AC voltage or a current, the average value is best expressed by the root mean square value, *provided the waveform is a perfect sine wave.* Note that "rms power" is meaningless. Power should be expressed as the product of rms current and rms voltage:

$$I/\sqrt{2} \times V/\sqrt{2} = P/2$$

Thus average power is *half* the peak power.

Rumble: The noise from the motor in a record-playing system. Not considered meaningful in high fidelity, since other harmful vibrations are usually worse than the rumble.

Sampling circuit: A digital circuit which transforms an analog signal into digital data by regularly checking the status of the signal, and noting the data.

Sampling rate: The frequency at which a sampling circuit does its sampling. The higher the rate, the more likely that the samples will allow accurate reconstruction of the the original signal.

Scrape flutter: In tape recording, an extremely fast speed variation caused by vibrations that travel longitudinally along the tape. Caused by poor mechanical design of the transport.

Signal: The *wanted* information, which, in high fidelity, is usually music and associated sounds. Anything else is considered to be *noise* and/or *distortion*.

Signal/noise ratio: The difference between the maximum allowable level of the *signal* and the background *noise*. Usually expressed in decibels. See *dynamic range*.

Sine wave: A pure tone, representing only one frequency. It is so called because, if you see the wave on an *oscilloscope,* it looks just like a graph of sine values. Sine waves are often used in testing, but of course music is not composed of sine waves.

Speed: The ability of a device (amplifier, speaker, etc.) to follow a quickly changing signal accurately. It is *not* directly related to frequency response.

Stereo: Short for *stereophonic.* Derived from the Greek word *stereos,* which means "solid." Stereo sound should be solid and three-dimensional. Unfortunately most record producers don't know that, and they do not make stereo recordings. They may use dozens of microphones, but they will typically assign *one* microphone to each instrument. What they are producing is two-channel monophonic sound.

Stylus: The diamond that rides in the groove of a record. Non-audiophiles often call it a *needle,* but needles are sharp. A stylus shouldn't be, if you value your records.

Subchassis: A part of a turntable system, suspended, usually by springs, above or below the main support of the turntable. The platter and arm, but not the motor, are mounted on the subchassis. Because suspensions cost money, low-cost turntables don't have these niceties.

Subwoofer: A special loudspeaker designed to reproduce only very low frequencies, typically below 150 Hz. Subwoofers can be used to take the pressure off the main loudspeakers, allowing them to do a better job at other frequencies. They are also used in video systems to exaggerate very low bass.

Tangential tone arm: An arm which slides along a straight track, instead of pivoting, so that its pickup can remain always tangent to the record groove. A tangential arm (also called a *straight tracking arm)* is extraordinary difficult to design and make, and not surprisingly nearly all of them are trash. The few exceptions are costly.

Time distortion: An alteration in the *timing* of sounds, particularly in relation to one another. Time distortion is not often measured, but it is clearly audible. A (seemingly) little-known fact is that correcting an error in amplitude gets you an error in time. The relationship is rooted in physics, and there is no workaround. Equalizers can be thought of as generators of time distortion.

Transient intermodulation distortion: Distortion caused by the inability of an amplifier to follow a quickly-changing signal. Abbreviated TIM or TID.

Triode: A vacuum tube with three elements: plate, cathode and control grid.

Torlyte: A proprietary panel that seems to be made of light wood, but actually contains a labyrinth of small tunnels. It is used typically in turntable stands and other supports, in order to dissipate (and not transmit) unwanted acoustical energy. Especially popular in British products.

Tuner: An FM (and sometimes AM) radio, minus its amplifier and speaker. Used in an audio system to bring in radio stations.

Tweeter: A loudspeaker designed to reproduce high frequencies, typically above 1.5 kHz.

van den Hul: A European corporation that manufactures different products, from cables to phono pickups. Best known for the stylus which bears its name, which is offered by various companies, making it under license. The *van den Hul* stylus has an unusual shape which can play the entire side wall of a record groove, rather than only a part of it. There are competing designs, which are know collectively as *line contact* stylii.

Vertical tracking angle: The vertical angle between a phono pickup and the surface of the record. The international standard requires that the generating elements of the pickup should be canted forward 15°, which actually means the pickup body should be parallel to the record surface. Most records are actually cut at a sharper record, however, and it is best to cant the pickup forward at a slight angle.

Voltage: The force propelling an electrical current. Note that high voltage, in the absence of current, means little. A static electrical discharge may pack 100,000 volts, but the current is infinitesimal, and therefore so is the power. That's why the discharge doesn't fry you.

Watts: The unit of power, which is electrical energy.

Weighting: Pronounced like "waiting," it is the alteration of data in an experimental situation so that it matches the model. For instance, a polling firm, if its sample has more women than men, will *weight* (exaggerate) the responses of the men in order to compensate. In the same way, in measurements of noise, or wow and flutter, it is common to weight frequencies to which the ear is believed to be less sensitive, and therefore to de-emphasize them.

Woofer: A speaker designed primarily to reproduce low frequencies, primarily below 200 Hz. Note that the "woofer" in many speakers actually reproduce sounds as high as 3 kHz, and would be more accurately called *woofer/midrange* speakers.

Wow: A relatively slow variation in the speed of a turntable or tape recorder. See *flutter*.

Appendix B

Alignment gauge

The gauge on the other side of this page is to be used in the lateral alignment of a tone arm and phono pickup. Do not cut it out of the book before *carefully* reading all of the instructions, starting on page 34.

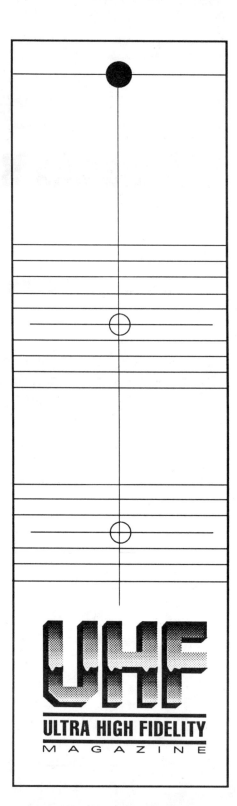

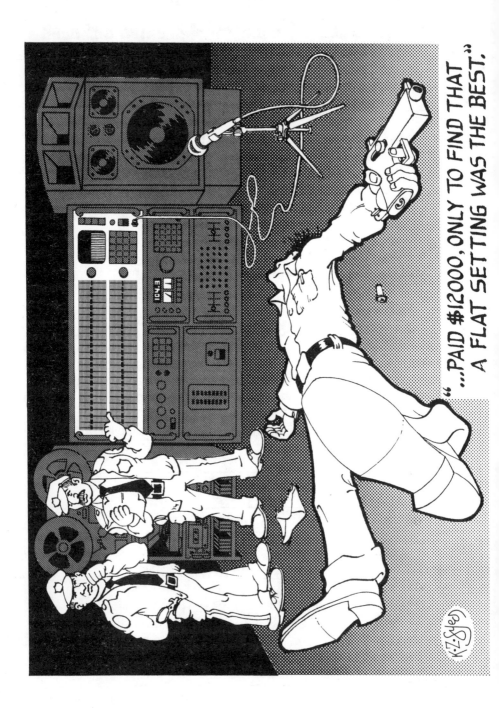

"...PAID $12000, ONLY TO FIND THAT A FLAT SETTING WAS THE BEST."